Computers
and
Pattern
Recognition

Computers
and
Pattern
Recognition

A. G. Arkadev
and E. M. Braverman

Translated from the Russian by
W. Turski
and J. D. Cowan

1967

THOMPSON BOOK COMPANY, INC.
Washington, D.C.

ACADEMIC PRESS INC. (LONDON) LTD.
BERKELEY SQUARE HOUSE
BERKELEY SQUARE
LONDON, W. 1.

United States Edition published by

THOMPSON BOOK COMPANY, INC.
NATIONAL PRESS BUILDING
WASHINGTON, D.C. 20004

Library of Congress Catalog Card Number: 66—29876

PRINTED IN HUNGARY

TRANSLATORS' PREFACE

The mechanization of processes hitherto performed only by Man, has in recent years, become part of a rapidly growing technology. One of these processes, a particularly important one, is that of pattern recognition. Many papers and monographs on this topic have been published in the West, devoted almost exclusively to work performed in the U.S. and Western Europe. There is a conspicuous lack of information concerning contemporary Soviet work in this field. The present monograph is intended to serve the purpose of acquainting English-speaking readers with an important aspect of Soviet work on pattern recognition, and its relation to relevant Western research.

The monograph is written in a semi-popular manner, and might serve as a general introduction to the topic.

We have resisted the temptation to edit the monograph or to extend the bibliography, in order to preserve as much as possible the nature of the original Russian edition. In certain cases (e.g. обучение transl. "training" or "learning") we have sacrificed veridicality for consistency with conventional English Terminology. However, we have not consciously changed the intended meaning of the Russian text.

August 1966

W. Turski
J. D. Cowan

CONTENTS

INTRODUCTION

The problem of "how do we distinguish male portraits from female ones", or letters "a" from letters "b", i.e. the problem of image recognition, is much more interesting and complicated than might at first appear. The peculiarity of the problem consists in that it is possible to learn to recognize arbitrarily many representatives of an image (e.g. any female portraits, as opposed to male ones, or a letter in all possible, handwritings) having seen only a few examples (e.g. a few portraits or a few sketches of a letter).

The ability to learn to recognize images, like, on the whole, the ability to generalize and to think abstractly, has always been considered an integral prerogative of the human mind. Hence it is only natural that great interest has been aroused by the possibility of constructing machines capable of learning to recognize images (or, as we shall say in future, "cognitive" machines) and even more so by the first attempts to build and test such machines. The reasons for this interest are obviously more complex than sheer novelty. Quite early practical applications became apparent: such machines could be used as "reading" automata, diagnostic systems, devices for interpretation of aerophotographs etc.

Besides, the problem of the creation of cognitive machines is interesting not only from the applied point of view. Since these machines allow one to simulate a not-well-known psychological process they may turn out to be quite helpful for studies of the operation of higher nervous systems.

It is a characteristic of the extensive literature on the subject of cognitive machines that it contains an amazing variety of points of view and approaches to practical and theoretical problems; many practical achievements seem to be the outcome of successful guesswork. For example, the famous "Perceptron" constructed by the American scientist F. Rosenblatt had "learned" to recognize visual images long before than it became clear how it was achieved.

In the present book we take as a basis of exposition, a rather general concept introduced by one of the authors (E. M. Braverman) — the so-called *image compactness hypothesis*. This concept underlies the design and construction of the cognitive machines described in the book, and allows one to outline methods for their improvement. On the other hand it provides a convenient way of explaining the action of some other cognitive machines constructed elsewhere. This book includes also the experimental results obtained by E.M. Braverman in cooperation with O. A. Bashkirov and I. B. Muchnik.

The authors have considered it necessary to provide general information on cognitive machines for specialists working in adjacent fields of research: biologists, psychologists, medics, who, from various points of view, are interested in these machines, but are not always able to comprehend the specialised cybernetic literature. This book should be comprehensible to any reader familiar with secondary school mathematics.

As we mentioned before, the book is based on the work of one particular school; the work of other designers of cognitive machines is described only to such an extent as to permit their discussion in terms of the compactness hypothesis and in terms of ideas derived from it. Consequently, the book does not pretend to be a full survey of cognitive machine problems.

Besides the approach described in this book (which may be called a "geometrical" approach), other approaches are being elaborated. Among these, the most promising seems to be that based on the study of statistical properties of the images to be recognized [9 – 13].

Attempts to simulate the recognition process in greater detail lead to the problem of the separation of useful features of figures. One possible solution to this problem is considered in the last chapter of the book. From the papers available which are devoted to this problem, one should note particularly the references [14, 15].

The most immediate practical results will be achieved, apparently, in the research based on recognition via *a priori* programmed distinguishing features [16−25].

The list of references appended to this book was not meant by the authors to be in any way an exhaustive bibliography of the subject of cognitive machines. The list contains only that minimum, which, in the authors' opinion, may serve as an initial reading for a reader seriously interested in the problems considered in this book.

A. G. ARKADEV

E. M. BRAVERMAN

Chapter I

THE IMAGE CONCEPT

When perceiving the phenomena of the external world we always classify them, that is we divide them (objects, situations) into groups of "similar" phenomena ("similar" but not identical). For one reason or another it may be necessary to relate to the same group, phenomena or objects which may differ considerably but have something in common. For example, all characters depicted in Fig. 1 are called "letter A" in spite of big differences in their shape. It is important, having singled out such groups or sets[1] of objects that we become able to "recognize" new objects, that is, to relate newly encountered phenomena to the existing sets. We can, for example, recognize the letters written in an as yet unknown handwriting. Having under-

FIG. 1

stood the idea of "letter A" (this is achieved generally after inspection of a few examples) we are able to recognize an

---

[1] Here, and in what follows, we use the term "set" in its mathematical meaning — it denotes a collection of objects somehow defined. Such a set may consist of infinitely many members (elements), e.g. "numbers", "atoms in Universe", of a finite number of elements, such as "books in my library" or it may contain no elements whatsoever, as "immortal man".

arbitrarily large number of other examples[2] of "letter A". This is of course true also for other letters, digits, and other sets of objects and phenomena.

However, it is not generally true that all sets of objects permit the recognition of arbitrarily many *a priori* unknown objects, on the basis of inspection of a small part of the set. For example, photographs of the readers of this book comprise a certain set. However, after looking at the pictures of, say, ten people who read it, we should not be able to tell by looking at another person's photograph whether he had read it too.

Thus there exist sets of a special type. These sets possess the characteristic property that people (and animals) who have acquainted themselves with finite numbers of objects from such sets are able to recognize (that is single out from various things and phenomena) arbitrarily many other representatives of this set. Sets with this property will be called *images*. From this definition it follows that our understanding of the term "image" differs from that adopted in epistemology.

As examples of images we can take the sets: "male and female portraits", "portraits of Pushkin", "Vrubel's paintings", "letters a", "numerals 5". We are able to use the term "image" in this sense because "getting acquainted" with an image does not involve memorizing individual objects, and the recognition of a new object is done without it being compared with all previously known objects. Apparently, in our minds, the general concept of a group of similar phenomena is formed, and images of these groups are conceived which allow us to classify infinite sets of objects from the acquisition of a finite number of samples.

The perception of phenomena in the form of images plays an important role in the process of cognition of the

---

[2] Concrete examples of elements of sets — for example "the first letter A on the fifth page of this book" — will henceforth be called "objects".

external world. It allows us to utilize our memory in a more economic way, freeing us from the necessity of having to memorize an infinity of concrete phenomena, and what seems most important, allows us to utilize the accumulated experience. Had we not the ability to group objects into images, we should be struck dumb by any new pheonomena, since none of them is an exact copy of any one previously examined. We should not be able to read an unfamiliar handwriting, to read books produced with a new type-face, and strictly speaking, we should not be able to read at all, since neither in handwriting nor in typescript are there two absolutely identical letters (due to small imperfections in the process of typing and minute differences in the casts of letter-sets).

From the very definition of an image, the "recognition" of objects of an image is always preceded by a learning process. During this stage, we study a number of objects and receive from some other source (e.g. from a more experienced man, the "teacher") the information about the image to which the given object belongs. In this way, we learn to read (the teacher showing and naming letters and their concatenations), to distinguish music composed by Chopin from that of Shostakovich (a poster or a programme tells us the name of the composer), to recognize Vrubel's palette by one's first glance at a picture (at the beginning we read his name on frame plates). The characteristic property of images is in a sense objective: different people taught by different teachers by means of different groups of objects of an image, will in general tend to classify independently the same new objects in the same way. It is the very objectiveness of this property of images, this independence of the individual characteristics of those who learn which makes it possible for two different persons who attended different schools and had different teachers, to comprehend the same novel handwritten text. However, in spite of this objectiveness the images themselves are somehow diffused, since it is not always possible to answer unambiguously the question whether a given object belongs to a given image.

Figure 2 shows how, by means of very small changes, one can transform the numeral 3 into the numeral 5, so that between a "good" 3 and a "good" 5 we have a variety of characters. Some of them we are able to recognize as threes and fives, though not of the best quality; others, however we will not be able to classify in any particular way. Had we asked different people to separate such cha-

FIG. 2

racters into "fives", "threes" and "non numerals", not all the results would have been the same. This same ambiguity can be observed also for other sets — numerals, letters, etc.

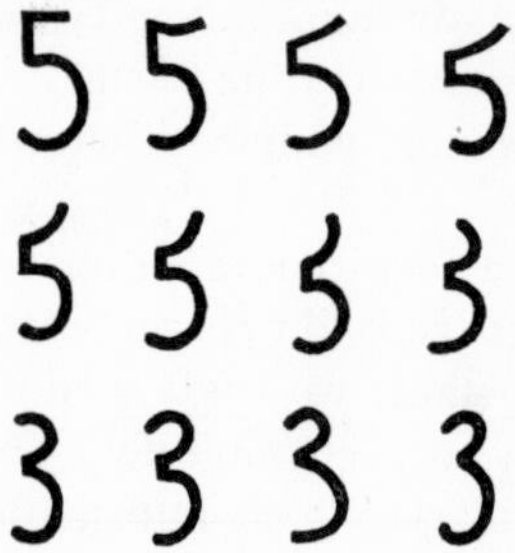

One way out of this difficulty is to resort to voting. We may agree, for example, to call an object "five", "seven", "letter a", etc., if a definitive majority, say at least 700 out of a 1000 people, are prepared to consider it as such. In what follows we shall suppose that boundaries of an image are defined in just this way.

Figure 2 serves to illustrate still another feature of objects of any image: we can change an object in a rather marked fashion, but it will remain an object of the same image. A "three" will not cease to be a "three" if we "bend" it a little or allow a small gap in its contour (cf. Fig. 3).

On the other hand, objects of images are not always equally stable with respect to the same set of distortions. Let us take as an example the second character in the middle row in Fig. 2. If we make very small changes in its upper part it will change from a "very bad five" into a "tolerable five" or a "very good three" or a "non-numeral". At the same time even considerable changes in its lower part will not prevent us from classifying it as a "five". A "good" five or three is much more stable: comparatively large changes

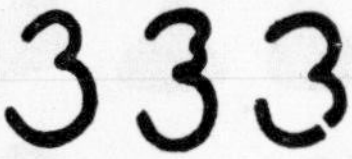

333

FIG. 3

are necessary in order to turn them into other numerals or into non-numerals.

From the fact that objects can be subject to more or less serious distortion without ceasing to be objects of the same image it follows that logical concepts are not images, e.g. the geometrical concepts of triangle or circle are not images. No matter how small the distortion of a circle, no matter how small a portion of a triangle's perimeter is left out, in the eyes of a mathematician they are no longer a circle or a triangle. However, in a general sense both a triangle and a circle are images; these indeed are the names we should use to denote the shapes depicted in Fig. 4.

The objective character of the basic property of images permits us to ask whether it is possible to simulate on a machine the process of learning to recognize images. We answer this question affirmatively. It is true that as yet, we can only build[1] machines which learn to recognize suf-

[1] The phrase "to build a machine" does not necessarily imply physical construction. In many cases it is enough to produce a programme for simulating a specialized (e.g. recognizing) machine on a universal digital computer.

ficiently simple visual images such as digits or letters. In other words, we know how to build a machine which would be able to learn to "read". Of course, one can ask whether this is worthwhile, whether one really needs to resort to the image concept in order to build a "reading" machine, i.e. a machine able to distinguish digits and letters. It seems that this end can be achieved by simpler means. One can, for example, store in the machine's memory the paradigms of all symbols to be distinguished, in which case

Fig. 4

the recognition of a novel symbol shown to the machine would consist in comparison of this symbol with all such paradigms.

Such machines may indeed be constructed. However, they would have one significant shortcoming. Since a machine's memory is in practice always limited, such machines would be able to "read" only a finite number of, say, typefaces and letter sizes. The increase in the number of "readable" characters would slow down the process of reading since each character to be recognized would be compared with an increased number of paradigms. Besides, such machines would be extremely sensitive to imperfections of printing, i.e. to many small, but diverse distortions of the symbols, which are practically impossible to avoid and/or predict.

Another principle of construction of reading machines is based on the distinction between some features of symbols being recognized. We can choose as distinguishing marks various features of symbols, e.g. their geometrical properties (characteristics of the curves of which symbols consist), topological properties (mutual positions of various elements of symbols) and so on. In some reading machines the recognition of letters and numerals is achieved by the application of the so-called "method of probes", that is by counting the number of intersections of the symbol with a special grid. Figure 5a shows one such grid used for recognition of arabic numerals. If numerals are projected onto the field with this grid (cf. Fig. 5b), it will be seen that each numeral

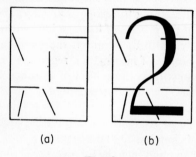

(a)   (b)

Fig. 5

intersects fully determined probes only, and the combination of intersected probes is different for each numeral. These combinations are used as distinguishing features according to which the numerals are classified.

Such machines can successfully read, say, typescript, but their capabilities are limited by the particular type-face for which the system of features was developed (and perhaps a group of similar type-faces).

Thus, the above principles of construction of reading machines are first of all specialized. Each machine can operate only upon a fully determined set of symbols to be recognized (e.g. numerals only or letters only) and only upon a fully determined type-face (or group of similar type-faces). Hence in changing to another type-face or from numerals-recognition to letter-recognition, it may be necessary to change the content of machine memory and/or machine structure.

A still more important shortcoming of these machines is that human effort (labour) is needed in order to prepare the collection of paradigms or the system of characteristic features. The quality of machine performance, i.e. the reliability of "recognition" of the demonstrated shapes depends on the quality of this preparatory work, and without human participation cannot be improved. In other words these are not learning machines.

We are, however, mainly interested simply in simulating the process of learning to recognize images. The expression "simulation of the process of learning" has for us the following, intuitively justified, meaning: the learning is not preceded by any input of information regarding images, whose recognition constitutes the subject of learning. The learning itself comprises the demonstration of a finite number of objects of each image. As a result of learning the machine should be able to recognize an arbitrarily large number of new objects belonging to those images.

We have in mind then the following experimental set up:

(a) no information concerning the images to be recognized is introduced into the machine prior to the learning process;

(b) in the course of learning, the machine is shown a number of objects from each of the images to be distinguished, and is informed to which of the images each particular object belongs;

(c) the information received is automatically processed;

(d) the machine is then able to recognize with sufficient reliability any number of novel objects from any of the images.

Machines working in accordance with this scheme will be called *cognitive* machines.

It is of some importance that the sets to be recognized in this scheme are called images. It has been shown above that not all sets permit a human being to recognize an infinite number of objects having studied only a finite number of examples. This is possible only in the case of the sets which we have called images, and that is why we resort to the notion of image when we try to create machines capable of recognition of simple shapes.

Were it possible to find some objective property possessed by any simple visual image and missing in sets which are not images, and were it also possible to describe this property formally, we might then possess the tool enabling us to build universal cognitive machines. Such machines would be universal in the sense that without any changes in their programmes and structures, they could be taught to recognize any images of the same complexity. Such machines would be able, after learning to recognize Cyrillic letters, to learn anew to recognize Roman letter-set or Arabic numerals.

It goes without saying that cognitive machines are of interest not only because of their comparatively narrow applications as reading machines, but because they help us to understand better the general pattern of learning processes in that the learning performed by cognitive machines is much more comprehensive than that of other learning machines investigated hitherto, e.g. machines simulating conditioned reflexes or self-adaptive controlling automata.

Devices simulating the development of conditioned reflexes respond by a finite number of reactions to a finite number of external stimuli. The process of "generation" of the conditioned reflex consists in trying out all possible reactions for each external stimulus and memorizing a "correct" one. In this case the "learning" is reduced to storing in the memory the relation between a finite number of *a priori* given external stimuli and a finite number of reactions, also known *a priori*. The relation itself is found by testing all possible combinations.

Self-adapting control systems or automata automatically find the maximum (or minimum) of a certain function which by assumption possesses just one maximum (or minimum) The simplest procedure for doing this can be described in the following way. At a certain point the device performs a number of differently directed experimental steps until one of them brings about an increase (or decrease if the minimum is desired) of the value of the function. After this the device transfers itself to a new point which corresponds to the "lucky" step and searches for a new "lucky" step starting this time from the new point. This procedure is continued until a point is found starting from which all steps are "unlucky". This point corresponds to the maximum (minimum) of the function. Nowadays much more efficient and reliable procedures have been devised for this task. The reader can learn about them from A. A. Feldbaum's book (27).

Cognitive machines are also of interest because they simulate a mental process whose mechanism is not yet quite clear; and since simulation of the activities of higher nervous systems is one of the recognized methods of investigation of the brain, the development of cognitive machines can also be useful in this direction.

Chapter 2

ENCODING TWO-DIMENSIONAL FIGURES
THE NOTION OF A COMPACT SET

1. Transformation of Pictures into Digital Codes

In order to feed a picture into a machine one has to translate it into machine language, i.e. encode it, or represent it by means of a combination of symbols on which the machine can operate. Encoding of flat figures may be performed in various ways. We have already mentioned that letters may be distinguished by the number of intersections they make with a fixed grid. In this case each letter shape can be identified by a code representing intersections of the contour with each line of the grid. The letters or numerals may be represented by equations of their constituent curves or by any one of a number of more or less artificial methods. However, we shall, try to use as "natural" a way as possible of encoding pictures. We shall draw our figures on a certain field divided by vertical and horizontal lines into identical elementary squares. The elements containing a part of the figure will be considered completely black, all others white. Let black elements be denoted by ones and white by zeroes. Let us also introduce a counting system for the squares — say rows are numbered from the top downwards and squares from left to right. Then each figure drawn on our field may be uniquely represented by a code consisting of as many digits (ones and zeroes) as there are elementary squares on our field. For instance, to the numeral 5 and the letter K

(Fig. 6) will correspond the codes:

"5" — 111111100000100000111100000010000001000001
0000011000100011100

"K" — 1000011000101001001010001100001100001 01000
100100100010100001

In general, the code of a figure can be represented by the formula

$$x_1 x_2 \ldots x_i \ldots x_n$$

where i is the ordinal number of an elementary square, n total number of squares and each x_i may be either 1 or 0.

In Fig. 6 we have used fields comprising comparatively few (60) elements, so that numerals and letters depicted in such fields have a "grainy" structure and differ from the ones that we normally see. This is, however, of rather

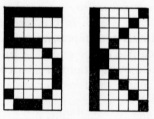

FIG. 6

secondary importance. By decreasing the size of individual squares and increasing their number, we can reproduce any shape arbitrarily closely. We all know that the discrete (dotted) reproduction of pictures in newspapers and on TV screens does not prevent us from seeing them as if they were continuous. By the same token, the particular way in which the field is divided and the shape of its elements are rather immaterial, since we can easily conceive a field of triangular, diamond-shaped, or hexagonal elements. We use a square net, the simplest one.

We consider this way of coding to be natural, because splitting the picture into elements is a basic feature of our own visual apparatus. Indeed, the retina consists of a great many sensitive elements (so called rods and cones) connected by neurons to the visual cortex. The lightsensitive elements of the retina send to the visual cortex, via inter-neurons signals whose intensities depends upon the illumination reaching each individual element. In such a way, pictures projected by the optical system of the eye onto the retina are broken down (via the rods and cones) into fragments and are transmitted element by element, in coded form, to the cortex.

This way of encoding pictures may be automatized in a sufficiently simple manner by means of a photo-electric model of the retina. If a picture is projected on-to a field consisting of photocells, the collection of out-put signals from such cells (i.e. electrical currents) com-prises a code of the picture. These signals can be subse-quently transferred into a machine which may be said to "see" flat figures.

Henceforth, we shall use the physiological term "recep-tor" to denote individual elements the field. The field itself will be called the receptor field.

The totality of all flat figures that can be represented on the receptor field comprises a set. Each concrete figure from this totality, e.g. K as depicted in Fig. 6, is an element of set. To each element corresponds, as we have seen, a fully determined code. In exactly the same fashion there corres-ponds to each of the codes a fully determined picture in the receptor field.

The one-to-one correspondence between codes and pictures allows us to concentrate on codes only, bearing in mind that a picture can always be reconstructed from its code.

2. THE RECEPTOR SPACE

Let us now introduce, by means of comparatively simple examples, some concepts that we shall use in what follows.

TABLE I

Receptor field	Figures	Codes
	x_1 x_2	x_1 x_2
	□ □	0 0
	■ □	1 0
x_1 x_2	□ ■	0 1
	■ ■	1 1

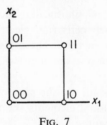

FIG. 7

To begin with, let us consider a very simple receptor field comprising two squares. The set of objects which can be represented on this field consists of four two-dimensional figures, shown together with their codes in Table I. Introduce rectangular co-ordinates x_1 and x_2 in the plane x_1x_2 which we shall call the receptor plane. To each of our four figures there corresponds one vertex of a unit square[1] in this plane. The co-ordinates of each vertex are equal to corresponding

[1] A unit square is the square with sides of unit length.

digits from the code of a figure (cf. Fig. 7). Thus we can find a correspondence between the set of figures that can be represented on the receptor field of two elements and another set, the set of points in two-dimensional space, i.e. in the

TABLE II

Receptor field	Figures	Codes	Receptor field	Figures	Codes
$x_1 \mid x_2 \mid x_3$	$x_1 \quad x_2 \quad x_3$ □ □ □	$x_1 x_2 x_3$ 0 0 0	$x_1 \mid x_2 \mid x_3$	$x_1 \quad x_2 \quad x_3$ ■ ■ □	$x_1 x_2 x_3$ 1 1 0
	■ □ □	1 0 0		■ □ ■	1 0 1
	□ ■ □	0 1 0		□ ■ ■	0 1 1
	□ □ ■	0 0 1		■ ■ ■	1 1 1

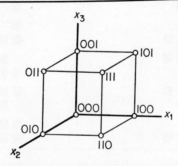

FIG. 8

receptor plane. Each of these points corresponds to a fully determined object from the set of figures.

Let us now consider a receptor field comprising three elementary squares x_1, x_2, x_3. Figures which may be represented on such a field and their codes are shown in Table II. We have already shown the relationship between the receptor field of two elements and the receptor plane and between pictures on that field and points in the receptor plane.

Similarly, a receptor field of three elements may be related to a three-dimensional space with co-ordinates x_1, x_2, x_3 (cf. Fig. 8). The collection of figures on the receptor field may be represented in the receptor space by the vertices of

TABLE III

Receptor field	Figures	Codes	Receptor field	Figures	Codes
		0000			1001
x_1 x_2 / x_3 x_4		1000	x_1 x_2 / x_3 x_4		1010
		0100			0101
		0010			1110
		0001			1011
		1100			0111
		0110			1101
		0011			1111

a unit cube. The co-ordinates of each of these vertices correspond to a code of one of the figures.

We now consider a receptor field of four elements (Table III). In order to interpret the figures represented on this field, we shall make use of a certain geometric abstraction: a four-dimensional receptor space with co-ordinates x_1, x_2, x_3, x_4. We can neither draw nor even really imagine a four-dimensional space, but this will not stop us giving to the figures of Table III a description analogous to that given previously.

To the set of figures in the receptor field of four elements
there corresponds the set of vertices of the four-dimensional
unit hypercube[1] in the four-dimensional receptor space. The
co-ordinates of these vertices correspond to codes of figures.
To each of the vertices there corresponds a fully determined
figure in the receptor field, and *per contra* to each of the
figures on the receptor field there corresponds one of the
vertices, namely that one whose co-ordinates are equal to
consecutive digits in the code of the figure. In general, when
we deal with a receptor field consisting of any number of
elements, say of n receptors, the figures which may be represented on it can be put into correspondence with points of
an n-dimensional space with co-ordinates $x_1, x_2, \ldots x_n$.
Exactly as in the above examples, one can exhibit a one-to-one
correspondence between these figures and the vertices of
an n-dimensional unit hypercube with co-ordinates equal
to code digits of the figures.

In order to represent, say, figures from Fig. 6, one needs
a sixty-dimensional receptor space.

3. COMPACT POINT SETS IN THE RECEPTOR SPACE

Let us return to a receptor field of two elements and
the corresponding receptor plane (cf. Fig. 7 and Table I).
Suppose we aim at separating in the receptor plane points
corresponding to the following two sets of figures: "figures
consisting of black squares only" and "figures whose left
hand-side square is white". The first set consists of just one
figure whose code is 11, the second set consists of two figures
with codes 00 and 01. The desired separation may be obtained by means of one line, and there are many ways of
constructing this line. For example, any one of the three
lines a, b, c in Fig. 9a may be used as the desired separatrice

---

[1] The prefix "hyper" is commonly used when naming geometrical
concepts in multidimensional spaces.

(point 10 does not belong to either of the two specified sets and its position with respect to the separating line is immaterial). Still more possibilities arise when we try to separate the set of "figures consisting of black squares only" (point 11)

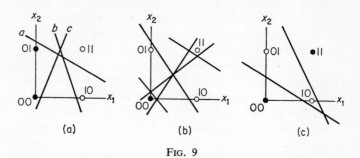

Fig. 9

from the set of "figures consisting of white squares only" (point 00). Any straight line passing between points 00 and 11 can serve as a separatrice (cf. Fig. 9b).

If, however, we try to separate the set of "figures consisting of identical squares" (00, 11) from the set of "figures consisting of different squares" (01, 10) this cannot be accomplished by means of just one straight line; at least two lines are needed (cf. Fig. 9c).

We shall now introduce the notion of internal and boundary points of sets. It will be noted that not all the points of the set (00, 01) are equally far away from the (only) point of the set (11). The code of the point 01 differs from that of 11 by one digit only, and thus the "distance" between these two points is one. The distance between points 00 and 11 is greater. We shall say that a point is an *internal* point of a set if no single "step" away from it transfers us to a point of another set; all single "steps" from an internal point lead either to points of the same set or to points which belong to none of the sets. If, at a unit distance from a point of the set, one can find at least one point belonging to another set, the former point is called a *boundary* point of the set. In other words, in the case of a boundary point, there is at least one digit, change of which (0 to 1 or 1 to 0) transfers the point into another set. Such digits are absent in the codes of internal points. This definition of internal and boundary points can be extended not only to points of two- and three-dimensional spaces but also to spaces with an arbitrary number of dimensions.

In accordance with this definition, the point 11 of the set (11) is a boundary point. The set (00, 01) contains the boundary point 01 and the internal point 00; the sets (11) and (00) have no boundary points; it is impossible to transfer from 00 to 11 (or *vice versa*) by changing just one digit in the code.

In the sets (00, 11) and (01, 10) all points are boundary points. Codes of all points of these sets contain digits, change of which transfers points from one set to another.

It should be pointed out that even in the case of the simplest figures of two elements, the fewer the boundary points contained in the sets, the easier are the sets separated. When we say that sets are easier to separate, we mean that the separatrice is simpler — say consists of one straight line rather than of two, and this line may be chosen in many ways (compare, from this point of view, Fig. 9b and c).

In order to separate points in a three-dimensional receptor space (Fig. 8), one should use surfaces, e.g. planes, instead of lines. Two sets, one consisting of the points 111, 101, 110 and 011, another of the points 000, 010, 100, and 001 can be separated by the plane shown in Fig. 10. Even simpler is the separation of the sets (000) and (111); indeed, any plane intersecting the interval connecting the point 000 and the point 111 will do. To separate the sets (111, 001, 100, 010) and (000, 011, 101, 110) is possible only if at least three planes are used. In three-dimensional space, again, the simplicity of the separating surface depends upon the number of boundary points; the sets (000) and (111) have no boundary points and it is very easy to separate them; however, when we separate sets (111, 101, 110, 011) and (000, 010, 100, 001) containing three boundary and one internal point each, we are much more restricted in our

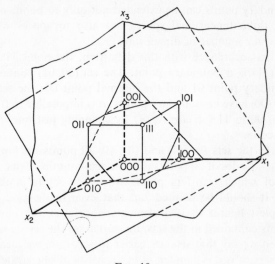

FIG. 10

choice of a separating plane; the sets (111, 001, 100, 010) and (000, 011, 101, 110) consisting of boundary points only, are the most difficult to separate, the separating surface consisting of at least three planes and our choice of these planes being still more restricted.

When separating points in n-dimensional space, we shall use hypersurfaces. Since it is impossible to present the n-dimensional space graphically, we shall use conventional two-dimensional illustrations. The points belonging to two sets to be separated will be represented by black and white circles; points which do not belong to any of these sets will be represented by circles with crosses. In a situation similar to that in Fig. 11a, the separation of sets is not particularly difficult. Any one of the hypersurfaces, represented conventionally in the figures by lines, and also many other surfaces passing through the same region of the space, will separate our sets. These surfaces will not be too complicated, too "wavy".

When points are distributed as shown in Fig. 11b, the separation becomes more difficult. We have to use more complicated surfaces and the number of different variants decreases. Furthermore, the separating property of a surface may be lost as a result of some comparatively small distortion in it.

Figure 11c shows a case where the points are "mixed" in such a way that the separation turns out to be extremely difficult. In order to separate black circles from white ones, we have to draw the separating surface next to almost all black points.

In the examples shown in Fig. 11, we can again detect the by now familiar property. The sets of Fig. 11a have few boundary points and are easily separated. The increase in the number of boundary points (Fig. 11b) makes the separation more difficult and, when the number of boundary points becomes large (cf. Fig. 11c, where almost all points are close to points from another set), the separation proves to be exceedingly difficult.

Let us now make our problem even more complicated. Suppose that we know only a fraction of the points from each of the sets. It is required that we should draw a separating surface on the basis of this fractional knowledge. Figure 12 represents the same sets as Fig. 11, but now we know only some of the points, say those which are marked by larger circles. The remaining points (i.e. the smaller circles) are unknown to us, i.e. we cannot use them in the process of drawing the separating surface. If the sets are like those shown in Fig. 12a, we can solve our problem quite successfully. The surface which separates the known points separates the remainder equally well (given that the known points are distributed more or less uniformly over the

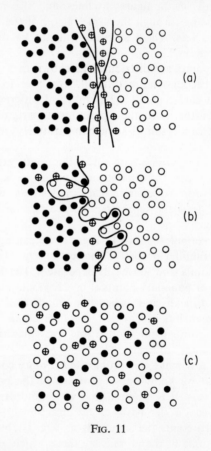

(a)

(b)

(c)

Fig. 11

regions occupied by each of our sets). However, if the sets are of the type presented in Fig. 12b, we should expect a far less satisfactory result. Having separated the known points, we may get a surface separating full sets quite erroneously. In the case of Fig. 12c, it is impossible to draw any satisfactory separating surface using the information provided only by the known points.

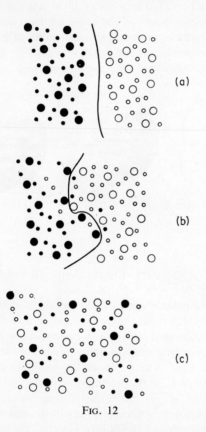

FIG. 12

The reason why it is so easy to separate the sets in Fig. 11a is that *points of each set form a compact group.* The number of points by which the sets touch each other (i.e. number of boundary points) is small compared to the total number of points. None of the sets has any part which would penetrate deeply within the limits of another set and the boundaries are smooth, without "teeth". In other words, every internal point of any one of these sets can be joined to another internal point of the same set by a smooth, fairly straight line which passes only through points of its "own" set.

Such properties permit one to attribute to the set with considerable assurance, the neighbourhoods of all points

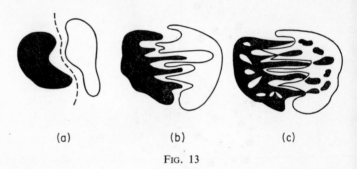

(a)   (b)   (c)

FIG. 13

known to be members, together with all unknown points that may be found in such neighbourhoods.

It is the *compactness*, i.e. the presence of the described properties, which makes the sets in Fig. 11a easily separable. The sets represented in Fig. 11b possess these properties to a lesser extent: the sets are more difficult to separate, and, if the separation is to be based on some points only (the known points), it might produce erroneous results. The sets shown in Fig. 11c do not possess those features at all: the sets are extremely difficult to separate, and, in cases of limited knowledge of the points, simply impossible.

In order to illustrate the point even more clearly, Fig. 13 shows, in a conventional manner, regions of space corresponding to: (a) compact, easily separable sets; (b) less compact, not so easily separable sets; (c) non-compact, difficult to separate sets.

To summarize:

1. To the set of figures in the receptor field, there corresponds the set of points in n-dimensional receptor space with co-ordinates $x_1, x_2, \ldots x_n$, the latter set comprising the vertices of the unit n-dimensional hypercube. The co-ordinates of each vertex are equal to corresponding digits in the code of a figure.

Conversely, to each vertex of the n-dimensional cube in the receptor space there corresponds a fully determined flat figure which may be uniquely reproduced from co-ordinates of the vertex, i.e. from the code of the figure.

2. A point in receptor space is called an *internal* point of a set if, in its code, there are no digits such that the change of just one of them transfers the point to another set.

3. A point in the receptor space is called a *boundary* point of a set if its code has at least one digit such that change of it transfers the point to another set.

4. If a set (a) has many fewer boundary than internal points, and (b) any two internal points of the set can be connected by a sufficiently smooth line passing exclusively through the points of the same set, and, as an effect of this, (c) almost all internal points have sufficiently large neighbourhoods containing points of only their "own" set then such a set is called *compact*.

5. Compact sets can be separated by sufficiently simple surfaces. Such surfaces may be drawn fairly precisely even if only a subset of the points of the sets is known.

This method of coding two-dimensional figures is well suited to black and white figures, each element of which can be either black or white. Correspondingly, the codes contain two digits only, zeroes and ones, and the receptor space is discrete, since each of its co-ordinates may assume only two values. The points of the discrete receptor space which result from black-and-white figures correspond to the vertices only of a unit hypercube.

This method can be extended to figures containing different shades of gray, as well as black and white. In such a case, each position of the code of a figure would be a number in the interval 0 through 1. Zero corresponds to white, one to black, intermediate values to different shades of grey. The receptor space is now continuous: each of its co-ordinates may assume any value within the prescribed limits. The points which correspond to figures, may take any position — on vertices, sides and within the volume of the unit hypercube. The exact mathematical exposition of this representation is to be found in reference (28).

The reader who has made himself familiar with the notion of a compact point set in discrete space will find it easy to imagine the compact set in the continuous multidimensional space.

4. The Hypothesis of the Compactness of Images

We can now state one of the basic ideas of this book, the so-called *hypothesis of the compactness of images*. This states: to a simple visual image there corresponds a compact set of points in the receptor space.

In order to illustrate the sense of this statement let us return to Fig. 2, representing the transformation of a "three" into a "five", and let us project the figures depicted in it onto the receptor field. The transformation of a "three" into a "five" can be performed much more gradually than in Fig. 2, i.e. in such a way that each figure will differ from a preceding one by only one element of the receptor field. To such a sequence of figures there will correspond a sequence of codes differing *(seriatim)* by only one digit, and a sequence of neighbouring points in the receptor space.

By means of a "voting" system (cf. Chapter 1), each of these sequences can be divided into three sets, corresponding to "fives", "non-digits" and "threes". Going from a "quite good" five towards "threes", we shall pass through a large number of "good", "passable" and "bad" fives until we reach "the worst" five. The expression "the worst five" means that if we change just one element it will cease to be a five.

Obviously, all fives through which we travelled, including the "worst" one, correspond to internal points of a certain point set in the receptor space. Only if the "worst five" can be transformed by means of very small changes (limit case — by means of one receptor), into a three rather than into a "non-digit", would the two figures ("the worst five"

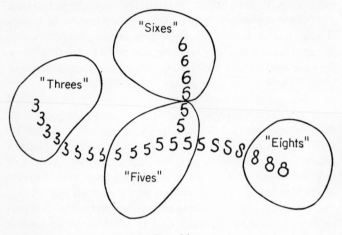

FIG. 14

and the three into which it can be transformed) correspond to boundary points in both sets.

We have considered the way from "fives" into "threes". Similar reasoning is valid also for ways from "fives" to "sixes", "eights" (cf. Fig. 14) and generally in any possible direction.

All we have said remains true no matter which letter, digit or other simple flat figure is taken as the initial point.

The compactness hypothesis is equivalent to the assumption that to a simple visual image (e.g. digits, letters, etc.) there correspond sets of points in the receptor space which possess the compactness property, i.e. the easily separable sets. In other words, to each image there corresponds an isolated set of points, and the sets of different images either touch each other in relatively few points (the number of boundary points is small) or do not touch at all, being separated by points which do not belong to any of the sets that correspond to individual images. The boundaries of the sets are smooth, not comb-like, the sets do not possess "peninsulas" extending deeply into other sets. The sets can be separated, each from the others, by relatively simple hypersurfaces.

The compactness hypothesis may turn out to be a very fruitful one. Indeed, if the hypothesis is true, then it reduces the problem of learning to recognize patterns to an already familiar problem of the construction of separating surfaces, given only a fraction of all the points of each image.

The course of such learning can generally be presented as follows. The machine is shown a number of objects from each image (say a few ones, twos, threes, etc. written by different people) and is told to which image the figures belong. The machine transforms the figures into points of receptor space and in some way constructs hypersurfaces separating the groups of known points of each object.

By virture of the compactness property, these hypersurfaces also separate, more or less reliably, the remaining points of different sets. As a result, the receptor space is divided into several regions concerning which it is known that each contains (in principle) only points corresponding to one definite image. This accomplishes the learning process.

If the machine is now shown an unfamiliar figure, all it has to do in order to recognized it, i.e. assign it to one of the images, is to transform the figure into a point in the receptor space and then to define in which region of the space this point belongs.

Is it possible to justify the compactness hypothesis? The direct proof is probably impossible since one would have to reproduce all the objects of all (or, at least, of some) simple visual images and determine whether corresponding point sets are compact. This is impossible because each image contains, practically speaking, an infinite number of objects.

Thus the only possible proof would be indirect. We can consider a hypothesis to be justified with sufficient reliability if two independent confirmations of it are available. The first confirmation will be obtained if using the hypothesis, it becomes possible to build up a sequence of mathematical

FIG. 15

and logical operations (an algorithm) for teaching a machine to recognize simple visual images.

As a second confirmation we may take experiments, the main content of which can be described as follows. Compact sets of flat figures are generated in an artifical way, and it is found empirically whether people and animals can learn to distinguish the sets, i.e. whether the sets are in fact images.

Compact sets of figures may be generated in the following way. One takes an arbitrary field divided into a number of elements, say a square divided into $20 \times 20 = 400$ cells.

Each of the cells is made either black or white, with probability 0·5. Having performed this operation twice, we obtain two different figures. As an example, we can take figures 1 and 3 in Fig. 15. After this, compact sets are generated "around" each of these initial figures. In order to do this, new figures are produced in such a way that each cell of the new figure is, with small probability (say 0·1), coloured differently from that cell in the original figure. As a result, one obtains figures each of which differs from the original by a small number of differently distributed cells (if we have 400 cells and the change of the state of the receptors is effected with probability 0·1 then new figures will, on the average, differ from the original by about 40 randomly distributed cells).

In this way, one can produce from given figures sufficiently many sets of figures, each differing a little from the initial one and each differing in a different way. To these sets there will correspond in the receptor space, compact groups of points.

Experience shows that such sets of figures do possess the image property. The reader may convince himself by way of Figs. 15 and 16, which represent figures produced in such a fashion. If a few people are asked to look at the pictures in Fig. 15 and are told that the first and second belong to the "first" class whereas the third and fourth belong to a "second" class and, afterwards, the same persons are asked to sort the pictures shown in Fig. 16 into these two classes, the majority of them will perform this operation in the same way. Pictures 2, 3 and 6 will be placed into the "first" class, the remaining ones into the "second".[1]

Numerous experiments of this type performed with people and animals give positive results. This is one confirmation of the compactness hypothesis.

[1] It is easy to see that black elements in figures of the "second" class tend to be distributed evenly, whereas in the "first" class they cluster in the right-hand upper quarter of the big squares, and are much less dense in other parts.

FIG. 16

The following chapters of this book are devoted to the second confirmation, i.e. the construction of image recognizing algorithms based on the hypothesis.

Chapter 3

DISSECTING PLANES ALGORITHM

THE algorithm for teaching a machine to "recognize" images, based on the method of dissecting hyperplanes approximates to separating hypersurfaces by "pieces" of hyperplanes, and comprises the following operations:

A. Learning (creating separating surfaces)[1]

1. Drawing dissecting planes.
2. Deleting redundant planes.
3. Deleting redundant parts of planes.

B. Recognition of new objects.

1. GEOMETRICAL ILLUSTRATION OF THE ALGORITHM

To begin with we shall follow the construction of the algorithm for certain simplified geometrical examples. Let us suppose that our aim is to teach the machine to recognize three images[2] a, b and c. In the receptor space there correspond to these images three as yet unknown, objectively existing, compact point-sets. In Fig. 17 these sets are represented as the regions a, b and c.

---

[1] For simplicity we shall write "plane", "surface", instead of "hyperplane", "hypersurface".

[2] In general, there may be any number of images.

Drawing the Dissecting Planes

Codes of two points related to different images are fed to the machine. The machine stores co-ordinates of these points in the receptor space (points 1 and 2 in Fig. 18) and draws an arbitrary plane I, separating the points. The receptor space is now divided into two images. This division may be very poor — as is the case in Fig. 18, where the greater part of region *b* belongs to the half-space attributed to the image *a*.

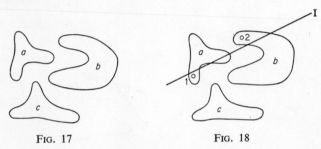

FIG. 17   FIG. 18

After the first plane is drawn, a third object is presented to the machine. There are now two possibilities: (1) the object is related to either of the images *a* or *b* and falls into the half-space attributed to "proper" image. In this case the machine stores the co-ordinates of the object and is ready to accept the next one. (2) the new object is related to the image *c*, or being an object from the images *a* or *b* it falls into the "improper" half-space. In this case, one half-space contains points related to different images. We shall call such a case a *contradiction*. In our example, point 3 (Fig. 19) which is related to the image *a* falls into the half-space attributed previously to the image *b*, thus creating a contradiction[1] with point 2. (The points with which a new

[1] A method for the automatic discovery of such contradictions will be described later.

object produces a contradictions will be called its opponents.) The machine removes the contradiction by constructing plane II, thus separating the opponent (point 2) from
point 3. Now the machine attributes to the image *a*, the
regions *ABC* and *ABD*, and to the image *b* the region *DBE*
(Fig. 20).

The second plane being drawn, the number of parts into
which the receptor space is divided is greater than the
number of points presented. By drawing the subsequent

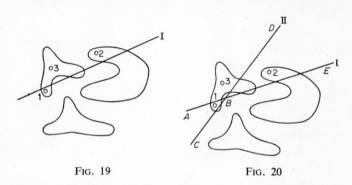

FIG. 19   FIG. 20

planes the number of partitions of the space increases very
rapidly (approximately as 2^n, where *n* is the number of
hyperplanes drawn): much faster than the number of points.
Thus the drawing of new planes while refining the boundaries
of regions *a*, *b*, and *c*, produces at the same time a substantial
number of "empty" parts of the space, which cannot be
related to any of the images (e.g. region *CBE* in Fig. 20).
At this stage the appearance of a new point may lead to one
of three possible situations: (1) there will be a contradiction;
(2) there will be no contradiction because the point falls
into the "proper" part of the space; (3) there will be no
contradiction because the point falls into an "empty" part
of the space, not identified with any of the images. In the
last case, the machine stores the co-ordinates of the new

point and attributes the region containing the point, to the corresponding image. This is the case, for example, when point 4 appears in Fig. 21. There will also be no contradic-

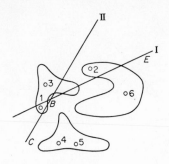

FIG. 21

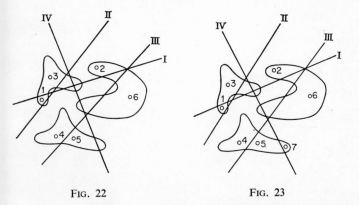

FIG. 22   FIG. 23

tion when point 5 appears. The machine will store the co-ordinates of points 4 and 5, will not draw any new planes, and will attribute region *CBE* to the image *c*.

However, when point 6 appears, it will create a contra-diction having two simultaneous opponents: points 5 and 4. First plane III is drawn to separate point 6 from point 4 and then plane IV, to separate 6 from 5 (Fig. 22). Point 7

(Fig. 23) produces the contradiction with point 6 which leads to the construction of plane V (Fig. 24). The point 8 falls into an empty part of the space, but it becomes an oppo-

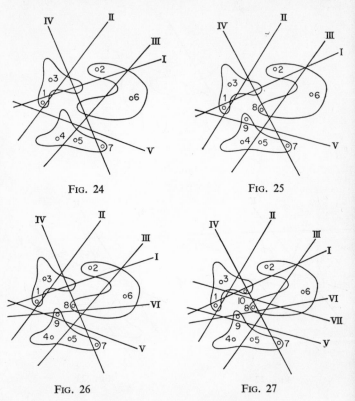

FIG. 24

FIG. 25

FIG. 26

FIG. 27

nent to the next point, 9 (Fig. 25). This contradiction is removed by plane VI (Fig. 26). The appearance of point 10, contradicting with point 8, causes plane VII to be constructed (Fig. 27).

It is noteworthy that with the increase in the number of objects fed to the machine and the quantity of drawn planes, contradictions tend to arise between objects and opponents situated closer and closer to the boundaries of regions *a*, *b* and *c*. The region where contradictions are possible becomes successively smaller, and the probability of contradiction decreases as a result of the decrease in the number of incorrectly identified regions. The frequence of contradictions may thus serve as a measure of the degree of accom-

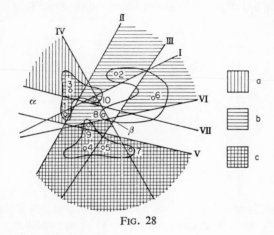

FIG. 28

plishment of the first stage of the algorithm. Let us terminate this stage by drawing plane VII. The situation arrived at is shown in Fig. 28. The space is divided into a number of regions, some of which contain at least one point and are thus related by the machine to corresponding images. These regions are indicated in Fig. 28 by various shadings. The remaining regions (which are much more numerous) have been left "empty" and are not attributed to any images.

It is quite clear that the learning process cannot be terminated at this point. A novel point (which is to be recognized) may fall into an "empty" region and thus it will not be possible to relate it to any object. It is necessary to identify all possible regions in some way. The continuation of the first stage of the algorithm will not achieve this object, however, since the number of "empty" regions will of course, exceed the number of given points by an ever increasing ratio.

Let us return to our basic idea, the assumption of compactness of the point-sets corresponding to images. By virtue of this assumption it is quite natural to relate the "empty" regions to images of adjacent identified regions. This opera-

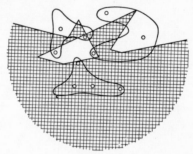

FIG. 29

tion on "empty" regions surrounded by identically identified parts of space is uniquely defined and will not¦ result in errors (e.g. the empty region α in Fig. 28 is uniquely related to the image a).

However, ambiguous situations may ensue for regions situated on the border of the sets and mistakes may be made, e.g. the empty region β (Fig. 28) may be wrongly related to image c.

The enlargement of identified regions of the space may be thought of as the deletion of parts of the planes which separate "empty" regions from adjacent identified ones. In addition parts of planes which separate similarly identified regions are superfluous and may be deleted. Those parts of planes remaining after this operation constitute the desired separating hypersurface.

It is of the utmost importance to distribute the deletion of parts of planes more or less uniformly over the space.

Violation of this rule may lead to incorrect separating surfaces. If, for example, starting from a certain identified
region we join to it all adjacent "empty" ones, and to the
region so constructed again join all adjacent "empty"
regions and so on, then, since after the first stage of the
algorithm, the identified regions constitute infrequent
"islands" amongst "empty" regions, it may happen that
almost all space will eventually be related to the same image
as the initial region. In Fig. 29 the shaded area represents
the region that may be related to image c by application
of this method (starting from one of the regions identified
by points of image c).

In order to achieve more or less uniform deletion of
parts of planes the following technique can be used. To begin
with, check whether there are any planes consisting entirely
of superfluous parts; if such planes exist delete them. Then
delete all unnecessary parts of one plane, then of the second,
etc. It can be proved that in this way all regions of the space
will eventually be identified.

Deletion of Redundant Planes

Let us return to Fig. 28. It is evident that planes I,
III and V may be removed. They do not contain any "bits",
deletion of which would result in complications. On remov-
ing these planes we arrive at the situation shown in Fig. 30.
None of the remaining planes can be deleted completely.
Each contains at least one fragment which if deleted, would
result in a contradiction.

Deletion of Redundant Fragments of Planes

Checking in turn all fragments of plane II, then all
fragments of plane IV etc. and deleting all fragments removal
of which does not result in a contradiction, we come to
the configuration shown in Fig. 31. The whole space is
divided into identified regions. The learning process is over.
In order to recognize a new object the machine now needs

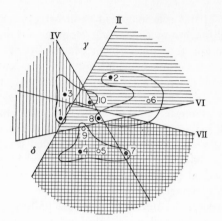

FIG. 30

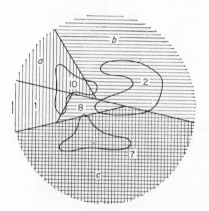

FIG. 31

only to determine to which of the regions of the space the point belongs which corresponds to this object. As is evident from Fig. 31, the division is by no means ideal. A substantial part of region *b* is attributed to image *c* and some "bits" of regions *a* and *c* are joined to the image *b*. This has occurred, because of the absence in the teaching sequence, of the points belonging to these parts of the space. If the learning process were longer, the relative area of incorrectly identified fragments (and thus the probability of incorrect recognition in the future) would perhaps have been smaller. However, the longer is the "teaching process" the larger is the machine memory required. There are also other means for increasing the reliability of recognition which we shall discuss in what follows.

2. DESCRIPTION OF THE ALGORITHM

The machine, of course, operates on numbers rather than diagrams. Let us follow the action of the machine for the same example (cf. Fig. 17).

Drawing the Dissecting Planes

Having stored the co-ordinates of two first points, the machine picks at random[1] n numbers λ_i ($i = 1, 2, \ldots, n$), where n is the dimensionality of the receptor space. After this the machine determines the values of two sums:

$$\sigma^{(1)} = \Sigma \lambda_i x_i^{(1)}$$

$$\text{and} \quad \sigma^{(2)} = \Sigma \lambda_i x_i^{(2)}$$

where $x_i^{(1)}$ denotes co-ordinates of the first point and $x_i^{(2)}$ those of the second one. After this the machine chooses, also at random, a number λ_{n+1}, in the interval defined by $\sigma^{(1)}$ and $\sigma^{(2)}$.

If we now form two new sums

$$\Sigma^{(1)} = \Sigma \lambda_i x_i^{(1)} - \lambda_{n+1}$$

$$\Sigma^{(2)} = \Sigma \lambda_i x_i^{(2)} - \lambda_{n+1}$$

[1] Random choice of co-efficients is achieved when each of the co-efficients may equally likely be any number from certain finite or infinite sequences. In order to achieve this end, machines use special generators (sources) of random numbers or of sequences of pseudo-random numbers. Considerations underlying these methods are outside the scope of the present book.

then taking into account the conditions imposed on the choice of λ_{n+1} one can easily see that one of these sums will necessarily be negative whereas the other one will be positive. The geometric interpretation of this is that the machine-determined numbers $\lambda_1, \lambda_2, \ldots, \lambda_{n+1}$, are co-efficients of a

TABLE IV

		Sign Table	
		Plane Number	
Point Number	Image	I	
		Sign of the point	
1	a	0	
2	b	1	

plane separating our two points. Indeed, substituting the co-ordinates of one of the points into the left hand side of the equation of this plane

$$\Sigma \lambda_i x_i - \lambda_{n+1} = 0$$

will give a negative value whereas substitution of the co-ordinates of the other point will result in a positive value. It is known that such an outcome will occur if the points are situated on opposite sides of the plane. Let us denote the position of a given point with respect to a given plane by the symbol "1" if on the substitution of the co-ordinates of this point into the left-hand side of the equation of the plane, one obtains a positive number, and otherwise by the symbol "0".

We say that the point has sign "1" or sign "0" with respect to the plane. Let us represent a part of machine memory, after the first separating plane is drawn (Fig. 18), in the form of Table IV, which we call — the sign table.

When the next (third) point appears (Fig. 19) the machine determines its sign relative to the first plane and fills the third row of the sign table (cf. Table V).

Afterwards the machine searches for opponents, i.e. sequentially compares the last row of the table with all

TABLE V

| | | Plane Number | |
| | | I | |
Point Number	Image	Sign of the point	
1	a	0	
2	b	1	
3	a	1	

TABLE VI

| | | Plane Number | | |
| | | I | II | |
Point Number	Image	Sign of the point		
1	a	0	1	
2	b	1	0	
3	a	1	1	

preceding ones. A contradiction occurs when two identical rows refer to different images.

In our case we have an obvious contradiction: the point 3, related to the image a, has fallen on the same side of plane I as the point 2 related to the image b. The machine constructs plane II, separating points 2 and 3 (Fig. 20) and computes the signs of all recorded points with respect to this plane. The sign table assumes the form of Table VI.

The contradiction is removed.

Now there appear points 4, 5 and 6 (Fig. 21). After computation of their signs we arrive at Table VII. The

TABLE VII

Point Number	Image	Plane Number		
		I	II	
		Sign of the point		
1	a	0	1	
2	b	1	0	
3	a	1	1	
4	c	0	0	
5	c	0	0	
6	b	0	0	

TABLE VIII

Sign Table

Point Number	Image	Plane Number			
		I	II	III	IV
		Sign of the point			
1	a	0	1	1	1
2	b	1	0	1	0
3	a	1	1	1	1
4	c	0	0	1	1
5	c	0	0	0	1
6	b	0	0	0	0

search for opponents after the occurrence of point 4 and then point 5 results in no contradictions. However, after point 6 has appeared a contradiction arises. Point 6 (image *b*) is on the same side of planes I and II as points 4 and 5 (image *c*). The plane III separating points 4 and 6 is drawn and after a new search for opponents − the plane IV is constructed separating points 6 and 5 (Fig. 22). The signs of all points relative to these new planes are recorded in Table VIII. The contradictions are again removed.

As new points appear the machine continues filling the sign table. Each new point leads to a new row in the table, each plane to a new column.

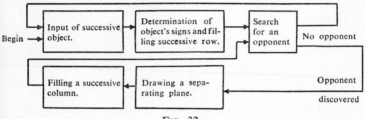

FIG. 32

The action of the machine at this stage may be described by means of the flow-chart shown in Fig. 32. As soon as an object is received, its signs with respect to all planes are determined, and the relevant row is filled after which the machine searches for opponents. This leads to one of two possibilities: if there is no opponent the machine receives the next object (upper loop of the flow-chart); if an opponent is discovered the machine draws a new plane and fills up the corresponding column. However, it may happen that there is more than one opponent, as indeed occurred in our example after the point 6 appeared. Thus after filling up a new column the machine returns to the search for opponents (lower loop of the flow-chart). The machine remains in the lower loop until all contradictions are removed. When this is achieved, the machine transfers to the upper loop and receives a new object.

The sign table after accomplishment of the first part of the algorithm is shown in Table IX. The contents of Table IX are equivalent to Fig. 28. Each row of the table corresponds to one of the shaded areas in Fig. 28 and represents a code of such regions, i.e. of a convex n-dimensional polyhedron formed by intersecting planes[1]. This code indicates on which side of each of the dissecting planes is situated the polyhedron containing the given point.

TABLE IX

Point Number	Image	Plane Number						
		I	II	III	IV	V	VI	VII
		Sign of the point						
1	a	0	1	1	1	0	1	1
2	b	1	0	1	0	0	1	0
3	a	1	1	1	1	0	1	0
4	c	0	0	1	1	1	0	1
5	c	0	0	0	1	1	0	1
6	b	0	0	0	0	0	1	0
7	c	0	0	0	0	1	0	1
8	b	0	0	1	1	0	1	1
9	c	0	0	1	1	0	0	1
10	a	0	0	1	1	0	1	0

Deletion of Redundant Planes

After the sign table is completed the machine passes over to the second stage of the algorithm; the flow-chart of this stage is given in Fig. 33. To begin with the column corresponding to the plane I is "removed" from the sign table. Following this the search for contradictions is initiated, i.e. consecutive comparison of each of the rows with all others. "Removal" of a column means that during this search, digits recorded in the column are disregarded. If no contradictions are discovered, i.e. no two rows are found to be identical and related to different images, the column is deleted from the machine memory. Otherwise the column

[1] We shall use the term polyhedron to denote both closed and open regions of space, the boundaries of which consist of parts of planes.

is „restored", that is its digits will be taken into account in further operations. The machine passes over to column II, columm III and so on till the last one. In our example,

TABLE X

		Plane Number			
Point Number	Image	II	IV	VI	VII
		Sign of the point			
1	a	0	1	1	1
2	b	1	0	1	0
3	a	1	1	1	0
4	c	0	1	0	1
5	c	0	1	0	1
6	b	0	0	1	0
7	c	0	0	0	1
8	b	0	1	1	1
9	c	0	1	0	1
10	a	0	1	1	0

(The first line under "Sign Table" caption applies.)

Sign Table

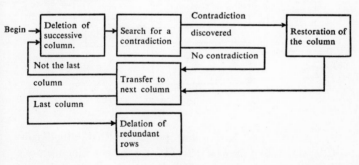

FIG. 33

after deletion of redundant columns I, III, and V the sign table assumes the form shown in Table X. In this table there are identical rows. This means that in the receptor space there are polyhedra containing more than one point (Fig. 30). Such

polyhedra can occur at the first stage of the algorithm and
after deletion of planes the number of these polyhedra could
increase. At the same time one point is quite sufficient to iden-

TABLE XI

Sign Table

Point Number	Image	Plane Number			
		II	IV	VI	VII
		Sign of the point			
1	a	1	1	1	1
2	b	0	0	1	0
3	a	1	1	1	0
4	c	0	1	0	1
7	c	0	0	0	1
8	b	0	1	1	1
10	a	0	1	1	0

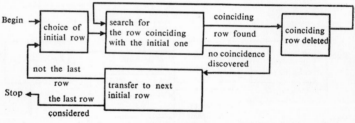

FIG. 34

tify a polyhedron. "Redundant" points (i.e. "redundant" rows
of the sign table) may be deleted from the machine memory.
Hence having considered deleting the last plane, the machine proceeds to delete redundant rows. The order in which
this task is carried through should be clear from Fig. 34.
After deletion of redundant rows we arrive at Table XI. In
Fig. 30 the points which remain after deletion of redundant
rows are denoted by full circles.

Deletion of Redundant Fragments of Planes

We have previously agreed to remove at first, redundant fragments of one plane, then of another, etc. Consider the plane II (Fig. 30). Its redundant fragments are borders between the polyhedrons 2 and γ, 3 and 10, 4 and δ^1. If we remove these boundaries the similarly identified polyhedra 3 and 10 will be united into one region of space, the polyhedron γ will be joined to the polyhedron 2 and the polyhedron δ to polyhedron 4.

As has been mentioned before, the rows of the sign table are codes of identified polyhedra. The digits of these codes indicate on which side of each of the planes is situated a given polyhedron and all points contained in it. Polyhedra separated by only one fragment of one plane have codes differing in only one position, and this position corresponds to the plane which separates them. That this is so can be seen by inspection of Table XI and Fig. 30, e.g. polyhedra 3 and 10, 10 and 8, 8 and 4, 4 and 7.

Let us anticipate a little and consider the operation of the machine when recognizing a new object. When a new object appears, the machine, naturally, should compute its signs with respect to all planes and compare the code obtained with all rows of the sign table. If the point corresponding to the new object falls for example into polyhedron 2, its code will coincide with the second row of the sign table and the object will be attributed to the image *b*. The object, whose point falls into the polyhedron γ joined to the image *b*, i.e. whose code differs from the code of polyhedron 2 in the first position (corresponding to plane II), should also be attributed to the image *b*. In other words, the deletion of the fragment of the plane II between the polyhedra 2 and γ is equivalent to the statement that the first position of the code of the polyhedron 2 is insignificant and may be ignored

---

[1] We shall name identified polyhedra by the ordinal numbers of the points they contain and "empty" ones by Greek letters.

during the recognition of new objects. Coincidence in the remaining   positions suffices to attribute an object to the image b.

TABLE XII

	Position Table			
Point Number	Plane Number			
	II	IV	VI	VII
1	0	1	0	0
2	1	0	1	0
3	1	0	1	0
4	1	1	0	0
7	1	1	0	0
8	0	1	0	0
10	1	0	1	0

The removal of all indicated fragments of plane II means that in the second column of the sign table the positions on the intersection of the rows 2, 3, 4, 7 and 10 are insignificant. Digits in the rows 1 and 8 are significant, as their corresponding polyhedra 1 and 8 belong to different images and the fragment of plane II which separates them cannot be removed (cf. Fig. 30). The impossibility of deleting plane II follows also from Table XI: if column II is removed then polyhedra 1 and 8 attributed to different images, will have identical codes, which of course must be avoided.

From the foregoing, it clearly follows that deletion of redundant fragments of planes reduces to the construction of the table of *significant* and *insignificant* positions for all rows of the sign table. In this new table (called the position table) we shall put a one (1) in the locations corresponding to insignificant positions of the sign table and zero (0) elsewhere. The construction of the position table is carried out as follows. In the initial location of its first column we place a one. This is equivalent to the removal of this fragment

of plane II which delimits the polyhedron 1, i.e. it is equivalent to joining this polyhedron with polyhedron 8. Then
we check to see whether this can be justified by searching

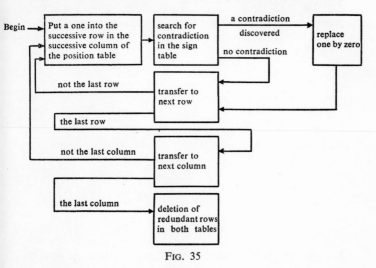

FIG. 35

for contradictions in the sign table, i.e. in comparing digits
of the first row with corresponding digits of other rows.
If no contradiction (agreement of rows related to different
images) is discovered, the machine passes to the second row
of the first column and places a one therein. If, however,
a contradiction is discovered, then before transferring to the
second row, the machine replaces the one in the first row
by zero. After this the machine resumes the search for contradictions in the sign table, according to the flow chart
shown in Fig. 35. During the investigation of the second and
following columns, each of the two rows being compared
at any given moment may already contain some insignificant
digits (marked by ones in the position table). Hence the
comparison is performed only on those positions which
are significant in both rows.

It is left to the reader to confirm that after filling elements in the last column the position table assumes the form of Table XII. After the position table is completed it may be that the sign table contains rows differing by insignificant digits only (i.e. having the same significant digits). To these

TABLE XIII

		Plane Number			
Point Number	Image	II	IV	VI	VII
		Sign of the point			
1	a	1	1	1	1
2	b	0	0	1	0
7	c	0	0	0	1
8	b	0	1	1	1
10	a	0	1	1	0

Sign Table

rows there will correspond identical rows in the position table. In our example such rows are 3 and 10, and 4 and 7. Of course, from each group of such rows all but one row may be deleted; this is done in fact, after completion of the position table (Fig. 35). The flow-chart of the process of deletion of redundant rows is quite similar to that of Fig. 34, but the search for coincident rows is carried out only with respect to significant positions.

In our example rows 3 and 4 will be deleted from both tables. The final form of the tables is shown in Tables XII and XIV. This completes the learning process.

The entire space is divided into three regions corresponding to the images, *a*, *b* and *c* (cf. Fig. 31). In order to prove that this division exhausts the space and that there are no "empty" unidentified regions left, we proceed as follows. It can easily be proved that every possible four-digit code,

0000 through 1111, coincides in significant positions with one of the rows of the sign table (Table XIII), hence any point in the receptor space falls into one of the three identified regions, i.e. there are no unidentified regions.

TABLE XIV

Position Table

Point Number	Plane Number			
	II	IV	VI	VII
1	0	1	0	0
2	1	0	1	0
7	1	1	0	0
8	0	1	0	0
10	1	0	1	0

Recognition of New Objects

When presented with a new object the machine computes its signs with respect to all planes and the resultant code is compared in significant positions consecutively with all rows of the sign table (Table XIII). When a coincidence is discovered the machine attributes the new object to the corresponding image.

3. EXPERIMENTAL RESULTS

Experiments were performed on the recognition of the numerals "0", "1", "2", "3" and "5". The numerals were represented on a receptor field comprising $6 \times 10 = 60$ elements, similar to the field shown in Fig. 6. Altogether, some 800 numerals were prepared, from which about one-quarter were used for teaching, the remainder being used for testing the correctness of recognition.

The experiments were carried out on a universal digital computer. The co-efficients of separating planes (except

numbers λ_{n+1}) were chosen from the set -1, 0, $+1$, the
choice being governed by a sequence of pseudorandom
numbers.

The algorithm described above has been implemented
in six different ways. The collection of numerals used for

TABLE XV

Index	Variant						Average value of index
	1	2	3	4	5	6	
Reliability of recognition (in %)	79·75	69	77·2	74·5	79	77	76
Memory volume after learning (in bits)	2172	3135	3495	2422	2977	3565	2961

Translator's footnote:
    "Bit" is used here in the usual sense to denote an elementary
cell in a computer memory.

training was always the same, thus the difference between
versions is due to randomness of the dissecting planes.

The results of experiments are collected in Table XV.

It follows from the table that the machine has "learned"
to recognize five different numerals. On the average 76%
of the numerals were recognized correctly and one of the
versions achieved almost 80% reliability.

Let us consider for a moment the index "memory volume
after learning". (This is to be understood as that volume of
the memory which is occupied by the *information* necessary
for recognition. The volume of memory used to store the
programme is not taken into account.)

In the first stage of algorithm the machine memory
stores the codes of all presented figures, co-efficients of all

dissecting planes and the full sign table (cf. Table IX). During the execution of the second stage of the algorithm, the requisite memory volume is greatly reduced since there is no need to store the codes of perceived figures. At the end of the second stage the volume decreases even more due to the deletion of the co-efficients of redundant planes.

The third stage of the algorithm initially increases the required memory volume when the digit table is constructed, but thereafter the volume is considerably reduced, since about half the rows are removed from both tables. This minimum memory volume, necessary for recognition of new figures is quoted in Table XV.

When the construction of a machine for systematic recognition of any particular images is undertaken, the learning may be accomplished by a universal digital computer with large memory capacity and the learned results (i.e. the sign and position tables obtained at the end of the third stage of the algorithm) transferred to a special purpose "cognitive" machine. The "memory volume after learning" indicates the required capacity of the memory store of such a specialized machine.

4. Ways of Increasing the Reliability of Recognition

The dissecting planes are drawn randomly and independently of each other. Thus if learning is performed several times on the same material (i.e. if several variants of this process are carried out as in Table XV) it would be highly improbable that errors in the division of the space would be identical in all variants. One would expect that in each variant the machine would err differently. This permits use of the method of parallel variants, by which several machines learn the same material simultaneously, independently of one another[1]. When recognizing a new object the machines will attribute it to some image, not necessarily the same in

---

[1] All machines may be simulated by one universal computer.

all variants. The final solution is achieved by "voting": the object is attributed to that image to which it has been attributed by a majority of the machines. Experiments indicate that the method of parallel variants is very effective.

Another way of increasing the reliability is by certain improvements in the method of drawing the dissecting planes. One can assume that if the dissecting planes are drawn close to the plane which passes through the midpoint between an object and its opponent and is perpendicular to the line connecting those two points[1], then the resultant separating surface will be close to the real border between images. The experiments confirm this assumption.

In the experiments with the "improved" algorithm the dissecting planes are drawn as follows:

A number k is chosen (the value of k is improved in the course of experiments), and after the co-efficients λ_i are chosen randomly the quantities $\sigma^{(1)}$ and $\sigma^{(2)}$ are computed (cf. the first stage of the algorithm) and the absolute value of the difference between $\sigma^{(1)}$ and $\sigma^{(2)}$ is compared with k. If $|\sigma^{(1)} - \sigma^{(2)}| > k$, the chosen values of λ_i are accepted and stored in the machine memory, if $|\sigma^{(1)} - \sigma^{(2)}| \leq k$, new values of λ_i are chosen and the process is repeated until the absolute value of the difference between $\sigma^{(1)}$ and $\sigma^{(2)}$ is greater than k. In addition to this the free term λ_{n+1} is computed from the formula

$$\lambda_{n+1} = \frac{\sigma^{(1)} + \sigma^{(2)}}{2}$$

The geometrical interpretation of these conditions is that the dissecting plane SS passes through the centre of the

[1] If we take as the dissecting plane just this plane, perpendicular to the line connecting an object and its opponent and passing half way between them, then for each fixed set of examples the outcome of learning is fully determined, all variants are identical and the method of parallel variants will not improve the reliability of learning. Thus, even when we systematize the drawing of dissecting planes, we have to allow a certain amount of randomness.

interval between the object and its opponent and falls within a certain angle AOB around the perpendicular to this interval, OC (Fig. 36), the angle being no greater than k.

In Table XVI the results of experiments with the "improved" algorithm are collected for $k = 2$ (variants $7-10$) and $k = 5$ (variants $11-17$). The average reliability figure

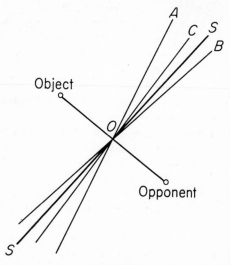

FIG. 36

has increased to about 80% with $k = 2$ and to more than 85% with $k = 5$. One of the variants with $k = 5$ gives a reliability of recognition of almost 90%. This sharp improvement in recognition reliability due to more systematic drawing of dissecting planes, indicates that the compactness hypothesis is true, at least in the case of the images employed. If this were not so, other methods of constructing the planes would have produced roughly the same effect.

The method of parallel variants further increases the reliability of recognition. The application of this method to the results presented in Table XV (original algorithm) allowed for correct recognition of 88·5%, and when this method was applied to variants of the improved algorithm (variants 11 − 17 of Table XVI) the reliability of recognition rose to 98·5%, i.e. the machine made a mistake in only 3 cases out of 200.

TABLE XVI

Index	Variant				Average for variants 7 − 10
	7	8	9	10	
Reliability of recognition (in %)	79	80	77·5	81·75	79·6
Memory volume after learning (in bits)	2646	2244	2590	3015	2624

Index	Variant							Average for variants 11 − 17
	11	12	13	14	15	16	17	
Reliability of recognition (in %)	84·25	89·6	84·25	86·5	87·5	82·5	89·6	85·5
Memory volume after learning (in bits)	1815	1310	2226	2646	1740	2016	2422	2025

The experiments thus indicate that the method of dissecting planes does indeed result in a machine able to recognize numerals. And since no information about properties of the numerals is given to the machine, the same algorithm (in principle) provides the possibility of the machine learning to recognize other images, of about the same complexity as Arabic numerals.

Chapter 4

ALGORITHMS BASED ON POTENTIALS METHODS

1. Potentials in the Receptor Space

An isolated electrical point charge generates, in a homogeneous medium, the electrostatic field represented in Fig. 37. The radial lines represent force-lines of the field and the concentric circles, lines of equal potential. In such a case the potential p of any point in the space is given by the expression

$$p = a \frac{q}{r^2}$$

where a is a certain fixed co-efficient, q is the magnitude of the charge, and r the distance between point and charge.

The change of potential with distance is given by the curve shown in Fig. 38. This curve and the above formula determine for any given magnitude of charge and distance between the charge and a given point, the value of potential at the point. It is also possible to solve an inverse problem: if the charge magnitude and value of potential at a given point are known, one can determine the distance from the point to the charge. Hence, the potential may serve as a measure of the distance between the point and the charge.

When the field is generated by several charges, the potential at every point of the field is equal to the sum of potentials generated at this point by all the charges. If the charges which generate the field form a compact cluster the potential will be large within this cluster and will decrease with increasing distance from it. In this case the potential at any point of the space characterizes the distance between the point and the cluster of charges as a whole.

Let us now suppose that there exist in the space two isolated compact clusters of charges. In one cluster the

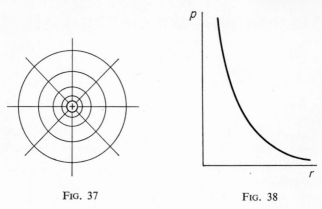

FIG. 37   FIG. 38

charges are negative; in the other one they are positive. Figure 39a shows the distribution of potential in the vicinity of these charges, the upper curve representing the potential generated by the positive charges, the lower one the potential generated by negative charges. It is quite natural to assume that a point is closer to that cluster of charges whose potential at the point is greatest (in absolute value). For example, point A in Fig. 39a is closer to the negative charges, whereas point B is closer to the positive ones. The point at which the potentials are equal may thus be considered as equidistant from both clusters. We assume that it is situated on the boundary separating both sets. In Fig. 39b, the potentials generated by both sets of charges are added algebraically. In this case points may be attributed to one or other set by the sign of the resultant potential at these points. The point at which the potential curve changes sign is situated on the boundary between the two sets of charges.

Let us now apply these ideas to points in the receptor space. We associate with each point appearing in the teaching process, a certain function, formally similar to electrostatic potential, i.e. a function which is greatest at a given point and decreases with increasing distance from it (this means

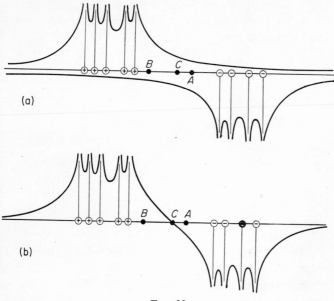

Fig. 39

that the point acts as a source of potential of a certain type). We may take as such a function, say,

$$\varphi(R) = \frac{1}{1 + \alpha R^2}$$

where α is the co-efficient determining the rate of decrease of φ, R- the "distance" between the point-source and the point where we compute the value of the potential, and where "distance" is defined in some convenient way.

The graph of such a function is shown in Fig. 40. As R we may take, e.g., the Euclidean distance between points (square root of the sum of differences in co-ordinates) or the so-called Hamming distance, equal to the number of differing digits in corresponding positions in the codes of both points. The quantity φ at each point of the receptor space may be considered to be a measure of the distance between this point and the source-point.

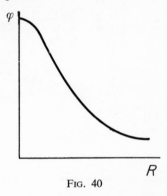

Fig. 40

Let us take as sources a set of points, e.g. the set of points identified during the teaching process as belonging to the image a. Then the mean potential generated by all these sources at a particular point of space, i.e. the total potential divided by the number of sources (image potential) will measure the distance of this particular point from the image as a whole (the division by number of sources is required in order to normalize the result).

Using this measure and the compactness hypothesis we proceed as follows. Suppose that in the learning process the machine memory has fixed two sets of points, corresponding to the two images a and b. Let a new point appear which is to be recognized. Mean potentials generated at this point by the sets a and b are computed. The new point will be attributed, naturally, to the image whose potential is greater at it. To describe geometrically the potentials method, we use the space of $n + 1$ dimensions, in which n co-ordinates correspond to n elements of the receptor field and we plot along the $n + 1$st co-ordinate the values of the potential. The potentials will then be represented in multidimensional relief, such that to each image there corresponds something like a mountain ridge having peaks in the region of internal points of an image and slopes falling down towards its

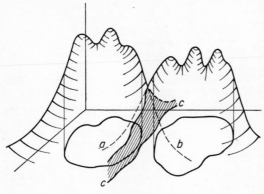

FIG. 41

boundary. The surface where the slopes of different images intersect, separates these images. The picture may be visualized as a three-dimensional relief (Fig. 41). The intersection of the surfaces representing potentials of the images "a" and "b" is indicated in this figure by a heavy line. The projection of this line on the plane creates the line cc separating both images.

The simplest recognition algorithm based on the potentials method may be realized in the following way.

1. Learning

During the learning process the codes of all given points are recorded together with the information concerning the membership of these points in corresponding images.

2. *Recognition*

(a) In order to recognize a point, the potentials of each image at this point are computed, i.e. the sums

$$\Phi_a = \frac{1}{n_a} \sum_{i=1}^{i=n_a} \varphi_{ai}$$

$$\Phi_b = \frac{1}{n_b} \sum_{i=1}^{i=n_b} \varphi_{bi}$$

$$\cdot \ \cdot \ \cdot \ \cdot \ \cdot \ \cdot \ \cdot \ \cdot \ \cdot \ \cdot \ \cdot$$

$$\Phi_m = \frac{1}{n_m} \sum_{i=1}^{i=n_m} \varphi_{mi}$$

are evaluated, where $a, b, \ldots m$ denote various images to be recognized, $n_a, n_b, \ldots, n_m$ are the numbers of points of each image shown during the teaching process, $\varphi_{ai} = \frac{1}{1 + \alpha R_{ai}^2}$ is the potential generated at the new point by the i-th point of the image a, $\varphi_{bi} = \frac{1}{1 + \alpha R_{bi}^2}$ — the potential generated at the new point by the ith point of the image b, etc.

(b) $\Phi_a, \Phi_b, \ldots, \Phi_m$ are compared and the new point is attributed to that image which generates the greatest potential at it.

In the simplest case, when there are two images to be distinguished, a and b, they are recognized by the sign of the function

$$\Delta\Phi = \Phi_a - \Phi_b$$

which takes positive values in the region of one image and negative values in the region of the other, and passes through zero in the vicinity of the boundary between them.

The curve in Fig. 42 presents the results of experiments on the recognition of ten digits, $(0, 1, 2, \ldots, 9)$ by means of the above algorithm. The reliability of recognition (percentage of correct recognitions) is plotted along the ordinate, the number N of samples of each digit shown in the teaching process along the abscissae. A relatively high percentage of correct answers has been achieved (about 85% on the average, for all ten digits). However, further improvement of the reliability is virtually impossible. At $N = 13$ the reliability curve is effectively parallel to the horizontal axis

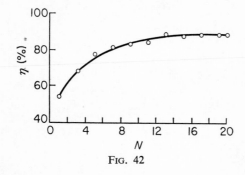

Fig. 42

and further increase of the training period does not improve the reliability of recognition.

The following explanation for this phenomenon is suggested. The algorithm would have achieved high reliability if the collection of figures used for training purposes was sufficiently "representative", i.e. reflected all the various figures of each image. In this case the points recorded by the machine during the training process would have been distributed more or less uniformly over the regions corresponding to each image (Fig. 43a). With such a uniform distribution of points the potential generated at any point of the region a by points of the region b would be smaller than the potential generated at the same point by the points of its "own" region.

It is, however, much more likely that training would not produce such a uniform distribution of points, and so their density within each region would not be uniform. For example, the maximal density of points might occur in those parts of each region which are closest to "rarely

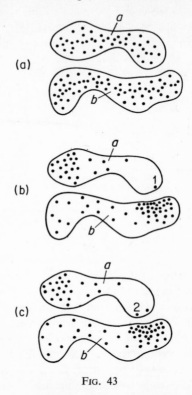

FIG. 43

populated" parts of another region (cf. Fig. 43b). In this case errors of recognition are quite likely. Indeed a new point 2 (Fig. 43c) will be incorrectly attributed to image *b* because it is situated closer to the main bulk of the points of *b* than to the main bulk of its "own" points. Moreover, the machine might not recognize an already "known" point, i.e. a point which was shown to it during training and was recorded in the machine memory. Indeed the argument we put forward concerning the point 2 holds true for the point 1 (Fig. 43b) which is a "known" point.

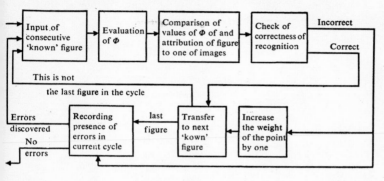

Fig. 44

Cases of incorrect recognition of "known" points have indeed occurred during tests of the algorithm.

The algorithm may be improved in the following manner. As soon as all the figures used for training have been shown to the machine, it is made to recognize the same figures and to check the correctness of this work. If an error occurs, i.e. a figure belonging to one image is attributed to another, the machine is instructed to augment the "weight" of the corresponding point by a certain amount, say by one. This means, that in future the potential generated by this point will be doubled (the denominator n in the formula for determination of Φ is left unchanged). After the first cycle of recognition of "known" figures, a second similar cycle is initiated, during which the weights of "unrecognized" points are increased again by one. These cycles are repeated as many times as are needed for correct recognition of all "known" figures (cf. the flow diagram of this part of the algorithm in Fig. 44). The essence of this improvement is that the distribution of points over regions becomes artifically uniform. The more dispersed and closer to a "strange" region are the points, the greater weight they acquire, as if their number increased. This means that the potential in the region with small density of points increases, thus improving the reliability of recognition.

TABLE XVII

Image	Number of objects used in experiments	Percent of correct answers			
		Simple algorithm		Improved algorithm	
		$N = 12$	$N = 21$	$N = 12$	$N = 21$
1	122	100	100	100	100
2	157	99·5	100	99·5	100
3	176	88·2	92·0	88·0	94·2
4	140	90·0	85·0	89·6	84·5
5	184	92·1	96·1	92·1	97·3
6	140	86·2	90·4	84·7	89·0
7	90	80·5	82·0	84·5	88·0
8	134	76·2	71·7	77·1	82·1
9	140	42·0	49·3	51·2	65·3
0	180	94·0	94·0	94·3	93·0
On the average for all images	—	85·0	85·0	86·1	89·3

Table XVII gives some results of experiments with the improved algorithm, compared with results obtained using the simple algorithm. The letter N, as in Fig. 42, denotes the number of representations of each digit shown during training. From this table, it follows that increasing N from 12 to 21, while not improving the reliability of recognition of the simple algorithm, leads to a considerable increase in the percentage of correct answers in the improved algorithm. It is worth noting that the most significant improvement is in those images which were badly recognized by the simple algorithm.

2. POTENTIALS IN THE RECEPTOR FIELD

In using potentials in the receptor space we have taken as the distance between two points either the number of different digits in their codes or the Euclidean distance between them.[1] These quantities, however, do not always

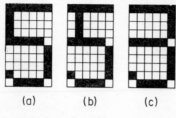

(a)   (b)   (c)

FIG. 45

correctly reflect differences between figures. In Fig. 45a, a "five" is projected on the receptor field. When the vertical stroke is shifted by one square to the right we get "worse" but nevertheless still "five" (Fig. 45b). If this vertical stroke is shifted to the right by five squares we obtain without doubt a "three" (Fig. 45c). At the same time, both these figures differ from the initial one by the same number of cells in the receptor field, and thus in the codes of both figures, there will be the same number of differing digits (six). In other words, a point from the "own" image (five, Fig. 45b) and a point from the "strange" one (three, Fig. 45c) are equidistant from the initial figure.

The shape represented in Fig. 46a may be reasonably assumed to be a "one". The "one" in Fig. 46b and "two" in Fig. 46c differ from it by the same number of digits (ten). Here again we have an example of the situation when

[1] These distances in case any point is a vertex of a unit hypercube differ from one another by a square root, for, if the first distance is q, the second is $\sqrt{q}$.

"own" and "strange" figures are equidistant from the original figure.

These examples show that the coding method we have adopted does not reflect differences in figures with sufficient accuracy. Considerable shifts over the receptor field of por-

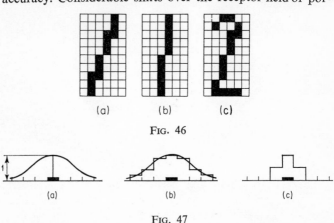

(a)   (b)   (c)

FIG. 46

(a)   (b)   (c)

FIG. 47

tions of figures leading as a rule to quite important distortions, give rise to changes in distances in the receptor space similar to those which are produced by small shifts, that do not (effectively) change the figures. These circumstances, naturally enough, cannot contribute to the reliability of recognition.

Evidently the reliability of recognition could be improved if methods of encoding were to be used which take account of the magnitude of any shifts occurring in the receptor field.

The following improved encoding method is suggested. Associate with every excited element in the receptor field a certain function equal to one on this element and decreasing with increasing distance away from it, i.e. a function similar to the potential φ with the difference however, that now the distance R between elements in the receptor *field* is measured (Fig. 47a). This function can be approximated by a steplike function (Fig. 47b), fixed within any particular receptor and changing quantally on the borders of receptors. Practice shows that with the "large grain" receptor field we have used, an even cruder approximation of potential would be effective. One can successfully replace the potential by

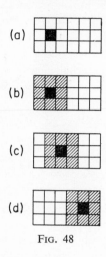

(a)

(b)

(c)

(d)

FIG. 48

a step-like function equal to one on the excited element, a fraction of one (say $\frac{1}{2}$) on adjacent elements and zero on all other elements (Fig. 47c).

Let us further assume that each position of the figure code can take other values besides zero and one, equal to the values of potential at corresponding elements of the receptor field. Then, for example, a figure comprising one excited element on an eighteen-element receptor field (Fig. 48a) would be represented as the step-like function shown in Fig. 48b, where the black square corresponds to one and the shaded squares to $\frac{1}{2}$. The code of this figure would be:

$$\tfrac{1}{2}\ \tfrac{1}{2}\ \tfrac{1}{2}\ 0\ 0\ 0\ \tfrac{1}{2}\ 1\ \tfrac{1}{2}\ 0\ 0\ 0\ \tfrac{1}{2}\ \tfrac{1}{2}\ \tfrac{1}{2}\ 0\ 0\ 0$$

Let us shift the excited element by one square to the right (Fig. 48c). We then obtain the figure represented by the code:

$$0 \; \tfrac{1}{2} \; \tfrac{1}{2} \; \tfrac{1}{2} \; 0 \; 0 \; 0 \; \tfrac{1}{2} \; 1 \; \tfrac{1}{2} \; 0 \; 0 \; 0 \; \tfrac{1}{2} \; \tfrac{1}{2} \; \tfrac{1}{2} \; 0 \; 0$$

We define the Euclidean distance between the figures shown in Figs. 48b and 48c as the square root of the sum of squares of differences between numbers in corresponding positions. Actual computation produces the value $\sqrt{2}$ for the distance. We now shift the excited element one more square to the right, obtaining the figure (Fig. 48d) coded as follows

$$0 \; 0 \; 0 \; \tfrac{1}{2} \; \tfrac{1}{2} \; \tfrac{1}{2} \; 0 \; 0 \; 0 \; \tfrac{1}{2} \; 1 \; \tfrac{1}{2} \; 0 \; 0 \; 0 \; \tfrac{1}{2} \; \tfrac{1}{2} \; \tfrac{1}{2}$$

The distance between this figure and that of Fig. 48b equals $\sqrt{6} = 2 \cdot 45$. As we can see, with such a coding method to greater distances in receptor field, correspond to greater distances in the receptor space. With our old method of coding the distances between any two figures from Fig. 48b, c, d, would be identical and equal to $\sqrt{2}$.

Let us now apply this new coding method to more complicated figures. We use the following rule: Each excited element of the receptor field has its "own" potential equal to one, and increases by $\tfrac{1}{2}$ the potentials of all (including already excited) elements adjoining it vertically, horizontally or diagonally.

Then, there will correspond to figures presented in Fig. 45a, b, c, the distribution of potentials in the receptor field shown in Fig. 49. The distance between two "fives" (cf. Fig. 45a and b) will be now equal to $2 \cdot 25$ whereas the distance between "five" (Fig. 45a) and "three" (Fig. 45c) is $5 \cdot 22$. Having applied this coding method to the figures shown in Fig. 46, we see that the distance between "ones" equals $3 \cdot 3$, between the leftmost "one" and "two" equals $6 \cdot 1$, between the middle "one" and "two", $4 \cdot 87$. Thus when potentials in the receptor field are used, the distances between objects of the same image are substantially smaller than distances between objects of different images, in spite of the fact that with the old encoding method these distances were equal. This is due to the fact that the new encoding method reflects better the relative positions of elements of figures

2	2·5	2	2	2	1·5
2·5	2·5	1·5	1·5	1·5	1
2	1·5	0	0	0	0
2·5	2·5	1·5	1·5	1	0·5
2	2·5	2	2	2	1
1	1·5	1·5	1·5	2	2
0	0	0	0	1·5	2
0·5	0·5	0	0	1·5	2
1·5	1·5	1·5	1·5	2	2
1	2	2	2	2	1

2	2·5	2·5	2	2	1·5
2	3	2·5	1·5	1·5	1
1·5	2	1·5	0	0	0
2	3	2·5	1·5	1	0·5
2	2·5	2·5	2	2	1
1	1·5	1·5	1·5	2	2
0	0	0	0	1·5	2
0·5	0·5	0	0	1·5	2
1·5	1·5	1·5	1·5	2	2
1	2	2	2	2	1

1·5	2	2	2	2·5	2
1	1·5	1·5	1·5	2·5	2·5
0	0	0	0	1·5	2
1	1·5	1·5	1·5	2	2
1·5	2	2	2	2	1·5
1	1·5	1·5	1·5	2	2
0	0	0	0	1·5	2
0·5	0·5	0	0	1·5	2
1·5	1·5	1·5	1·5	2	2
1	2	2	2	2	1

Fig. 49

in the receptor field, and consequently indicates better the differences between figures. This cannot fail to improve the reliability of recognition.

It is possible that something similar to potentials in receptor fields is realized in the human visual system as a result of the so-called "tremor" of the eyes. Indeed if the image of a small illuminated circle is projected onto the retina, then the total "exposure" time for the retinal elements situated close to the boundaries of the circle is smaller than the total exposure time of elements situated closer to its centre. As a result of this, the circle is received as a blurr with diffused borders (similar to Fig. 48c). Similarly, more complicated images are subject to similar transformations.

Table XVIII compares results obtained with the simplest algorithm with those obtained using the algorithm in which potentials in the receptor field are introduced, for $N = 12$. The average reliability of recognition has increased, following the introduction of potentials in the receptor field by 9% and has reached 94%. For individual images (those which

TABLE XVIII

| Image | Percent of correct answers | |
	Simplest algorithm	algorithm with potentials in receptor field
1	100	100
2	99·5	100
3	88·2	100
4	90·0	97·5
5	92·1	100
6	86·2	98·5
7	80·5	87·5
8	76·2	100
9	42·0	64·0
0	94·0	91·9
On the average for all images	85·0	94·0

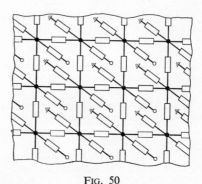

Fig. 50

are the most difficult to recognize) the improvement in reliability is $20-24\%$.

A technical realization of the method which uses potentials in the receptor field is shown in Fig. 50. If the terminals denoted by empty circles are connected to the outputs of photo-elements (receptors) then the distribution of potentials over nodes of the scheme (black circles) will be qualitatively identical with the distribution of potentials in the receptor field. For example, in case only one receptor is excited then the potential of the node connected to it will be maximal and the potentials of the remaining nodes will diminish away from the excited receptor. The potentials of nodes corresponding to two neighbouring excited receptors, will be greater than the potentials of the nodes corresponding to two non-adjacent receptors which are excited.

The electric potentials of the nodes of the scheme may be transmitted to the machine as the code of a figure.

Chapter 5

ALGORITHM OF THE PERCEPTRON

An American scientist, F. Rosenblatt, has designed a cognitive machine which he has called "Perceptron". Later A. Gamba, an Italian, proposed an interesting technical realization of this machine.

Whereas we based the development of the algorithms of cognitive machines on a certain property of images, namely the compactness hypothesis, Rosenblatt based the principles of the Perceptron on certain current ideas concerning the structure of the brain and visual system. As shown below, both approaches lead to similar algorithms for the functioning of cognitive machines.

1. STRUCTURE AND ALGORITHM OF THE PERCEPTRON

Let us consider the structure and performance of the Perceptron, i.e. Rosenblatt's MARK-1 machine. The Perceptron uses as its receiving organ a photoelectric model of the retina (Fig. 51), a receptor field comprising a few hundred photo-resistances. Each element of the receptor field may be in one of two possible states: excited or unexcited, depending on whether or not part of the contour of an object is projected onto the corresponding photoresistance. At the output of each element there appears a signal x_i ($i = 1, 2, \ldots, n$, where n is the number of elements) equal to one, if the element is excited, and zero otherwise.

The next level of the Perceptron comprises the so-called "associative elements" or A-elements. There are approximately as many A-elements (all identical) as there are receptors. Each A-element has many inputs and one output. When setting up the Perceptron before an experiment, the outputs of receptors are connected to the inputs of A-elements, each connection being either positive or negative.

The choice of receptors to be connected to a given A-element and the choice of sign of connections is random.

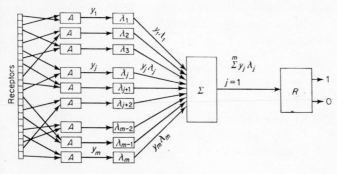

FIG. 51

During the experiment the connections between receptors and A-elements remain unchanged.

A-elements perform algebraic summation of the signals received by their inputs and compare the value obtained with a certain quantity θ, common to all A-elements. If the sum obtained is greater than θ, the given A-element is excited and there appears on its output the signal "one". If, on the other hand, the sum is smaller than θ, this A-element remains unexcited and its output signal is "zero". Thus the output signal of the jth A-element is

$$y_j = \begin{cases} 1, & \text{if } \left(\sum_{i=1}^{n} r_{ij} x_i - \Theta \right) \geq 0 \\ 0, & \text{if } \left(\sum_{i=1}^{n} r_{ij} x_i - \Theta \right) < 0 \end{cases}$$

where r_{ij} assumes the value $+1$ if the ith receptor is positively connected to the input of the jth A-element, -1 if the connection is negative, and 0 if the ith receptor is not connected to the jth A-element ($j = 1, 2, \ldots, m$ where m is number of A-elements).[1] The output signals of A-elements are multiplied in special devices (amplifiers) by certain variable coefficients λ_j. Each coefficient may be positive, negative or zero and changes independently of any others.

The output signals from these amplifiers are summed and the total signal

$$\sigma = \sum_{j=1}^{m} \lambda_j y_j$$

is transmitted to the so-called response element or R-element. If Σ is positive or zero, the R-element outputs 1, if Σ is negative, 0. Thus the output signal of the R-element (which is also the output signal of the Perceptron) is

$$R = \begin{cases} 1, & \text{if } \sum_{j=1}^{m} \lambda_j y_j \geq 0 \\[2mm] 0, & \text{if } \sum_{j=1}^{m} \lambda_j y_j < 0 \end{cases}$$

Let us suppose that figures belonging to two different images are projected onto the receptor field. If it is possible to bring the Perceptron into such a state that it produces the output signal 1, when figures from one image are projected, and 0 when figures from the other image are projected, this would mean that the Perceptron has learned to distinguish these two images.

The Perceptron as described, is able to distinguish objects from two sets only. In order to distinguish more images, say three images, a, b and c, a Perceptron built according to the scheme of Fig. 52 is required. The output

---

[1] In the MARK-1 Perceptron there are $n = 400$ receptors and $m = 512$ A-elements. Each A-element has 20 inputs.

of each A-element is transmitted to more than one amplifier (accordingly to the number of images to be distinguished). After multiplication by λ the output signals are transmitted to adders Σ, equal in number to the number of images to be distinguished. Instead of an R-element we have a device which compares the output signals of adders. The object is related to that image whose adder produces the biggest output signal.

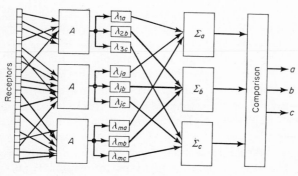

Fig. 52

In order to distinguish several images, yet another Perceptron could be used. In such a Perceptron A-elements are divided into several groups, each connected with its own adder and an R-element. The collection of output signals of the R-elements may be viewed as the ordinal number of the image, expressed in a binary code. This allows us to divide objects into several classes. For instance, in order to separate objects into 8 classes we must use three groups. In this case the following 8 configurations of output signals of three R-elements are possible: 000, 001, 010, 011, 100, 101, 110, 111. The appearance of any one of these combinations may be considered to attribute the object presented to one of the 8 images.

Each of the groups of A-elements, connected with its R-elements is structurally and functionally analogous to the Perceptron which is capable of distinguishing objects of two classes. In future we shall restrict ourselves to consideration of just such a Perceptron distinguishing two images.

Training the Perceptron is performed in a sequence of steps. At each step it is shown an object from one of the images. Depending on its reaction and following specified rules the coefficients λ_j are changed. It proves to be possible in a finite number of steps to train the Perceptron to recognize with sufficient reliability, objects presented to it.

There are two types of Perceptron training algorithm. The first does not take into account the correctness of the Perceptron's answers during the learning process, and the changes of λ_j on each step are executed irrespective of whether or not the Perceptron has recognized the last figure shown. In algorithms of the second kind the correctness of the answers is taken into account when changes of λ_j are made.

The algorithms of the first type are realized as follows. It is fixed *a priori* that after training the Perceptron should produce the output 1 when shown for example, objects of image *a*, and 0 when shown objects of image *b*. After this, objects of each image are presented. At each step the Perceptron responds to the presentation of an object by exciting certain A-elements. Training occurs when, at each given step, the coefficients λ_j of excited A-elements, are increased by a certain amount (say by one) if at this step an object of image *a* has been presented, and are decreased by the same amount if the object was of image *b*. It is evident that such a change of the coefficients λ_j should lead to an improvement in the reliability of the Perceptron's responses, for the increase in λ_j of excited elements brings about an increase of the signal at the input to the R-element, whereas a decrease in the relevant coefficients leads to a decrease of the input signal to the R-element. By virtue of the stated conditions, the Perceptron's responses are correct if image *a* is associated with positive and image *b* with negative signals on the input to the R-element.

Figure 53 shows the results of training the Perceptron MARK-1 to recognize 8 Roman letters, using the first algorithm. After $20-25$ presentations of different examples of each letter, a reliability of 70% is achieved. Further increase of the training period did not result in any further improvement in reliability.

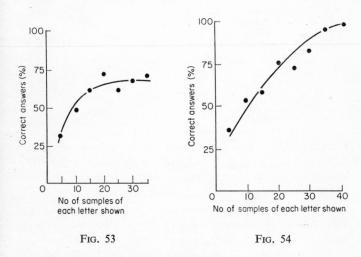

FIG. 53   FIG. 54

The second algorithm, as we have already noted, takes into account the accuracy of responses during training. When using this algorithm, the coefficients λ_j remain constant if the Perceptron correctly identifies the figure shown to it at a given step. The coefficients λ_j are changed only when the Perceptron's response is incorrect. As in the first algorithm the coefficients are changed in order to improve the reliability of responses. If, for example, the Perceptron incorrectly identifies an object of image *a* and produces zero on the output (instead of one), the coefficients of excited

A-elements are increased. If an object of image b has been presented and the Perceptron's response is one at the output of the R-element, then the coefficients of excited A-elements are decreased.[1]

The second algorithm produces much better results than the first. Figure 54 shows the results of application of the second algorithm to the recognition of eight Roman letters as before. After $35-40$ samples of each letter were shown, the reliability of recognition was almost 100%.

2. FUNCTIONS PERFORMED BY THE A-ELEMENTS

As we have noted the output signal of each A-element depends on the sign of the expression

$$\sum_{i=1}^{n} r_{ij} x_i - \Theta$$

where x_i is the output signal of ith receptor. For some combinations of x_i's this expression may assume positive values (or zero), and negative values for others. Each combination of x_i's corresponds to a definite figure projected onto the receptor field. Thus each A-element divides all figures which may be projected onto the receptor field into two classes. For figures of one class the output of the A-element is positive, negative for the other . This has a geometrical interpretation. Indeed, each combination of x_i's may be considered as the code of a figure shown to the Perceptron, or

---

[1] For the Perceptron shown in Fig. 52, the algorithm has a slightly different structure. The coefficients λ_j in such a Perceptron can only be increased. In algorithms of the first type, the λ_j corresponding to a given figure are increased at each step. For example, when an object of image b is shown, the coefficients λ_{ib} of all excited A-elements are increased; when the figure of image a is present, λ_{ia} are increased and so on. In algorithms of the second type the coefficients are increased in exactly the same fashion but only when the Perceptron's response is incorrect.

as the coordinates of a certain point in the receptor space. The expression

$$\sum_{i=1}^{n} r_{ij} x_i - \Theta$$

may be viewed as the left-hand side of the equation of a certain plane

$$\sum_{i=1}^{n} r_{ij} x_i - \Theta = 0$$

The sign of the output signal of the A-element tells us on which side of this plane is situated the point corresponding to the figure presented to the Perceptron.

Hence each A-element defines, as soon as the coefficients r_{ij} are fixed (i.e. when receptors are connected to its inputs), a certain plane in the receptor space.

All A-elements of the Perceptron divide the receptor space by means of m planes into a certain number of polyhedra (such a number is very large since there are hundreds of planes). This division is random, for the coefficients r_{ij} have been chosen at random.

To an arbitrary figure projected onto the receptor field there corresponds, in this experiment, a fully defined state of each of the Perceptron's A-elements. From the output signals of A-elements, i.e. from the sequence of quantities y_j we can construct an m-digit binary code, so that in the jth position of this code there will be a one if the jth A-element is excited and a zero otherwise.

The same code, describing the state of A-elements also describes the polyhedron into which falls the point corresponding to a given figure. A one in the jth position of the code indicates that the polyhedron is situated on one side of the jth plane; a zero indicates that it is situated on the other side.

At the input to the R-element, the sum of products of digits of this code by coefficients λ_j

$$\sum_{j=1}^{m} \lambda_j y_j$$

is produced.

At a given stage in the training period, i.e. with some specified combination of coefficients λ_j to some codes there will correspond a one on the output of the R-element; to others, a zero. This in turn means that some polyhedra are attributed by the Perceptron to the first class, whereas the remaining polyhedra are attributed to the second class. In other words, the Perceptron constructs, from fragments of randomly drawn dissecting planes, a separating boundary between two parts of the receptor space. The position of the boundary surface is defined by the set of coefficients λ_j at the given step.

The aim of training, obviously, should be to bring this surface closer to the real separating surface between two images (i.e. between corresponding point-sets in the receptor space).

3. An Example

Let us follow the performance of the Perceptron in a typical example when being trained according to the second algorithm. Suppose that there are two images, corresponding to regions a and b in the receptor space (Fig. 55). Let us assume that our Perceptron has 8 A-elements which are connected to receptors so that in the receptor-space there are 8 randomly situated planes I, II, . . . , VIII. These planes form 21 polyhedra, marked in our drawing by encircled numbers.

We determine by chance "positive" and "negative" sides of each of the planes. (In Fig. 55 the "positive" sides are marked by dashes.) This means that an A-element produces a one on the output if a point is situated on the "positive" side of the corresponding plane, and zero in the opposite case. We set the initial values of λ_j for all amplifiers to one, and require that the Perceptron's output of one corresponds to the image b, and that of zero to the image a.

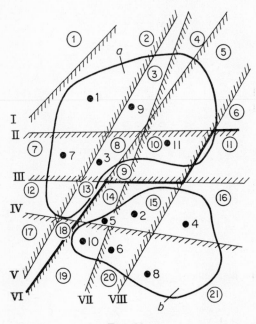

Fig. 55

Consider the state of the Perceptron (Table XIX) at the first stage of training after the first object of image a (point 1, falling into the 2nd polyhedron) has been shown. The Perceptron's "response" is incorrect (we have set the λ_j's so that all the space is attributed to the image b). The input to the R-element is greater than required, equalling $+4$. Thus, according to the second algorithm, all λ_j's of A-elements excited at this step should be decreased by 1.

TABLE XIX

	Step Number														
	1			2			3			4			5		
							Perceptron's state								
Ordinal numbers of A-elements (planes)	λ_j	y_j	$\lambda_j y_j$	λ_j	y_j	$\lambda_j y_j$	λ_j	y_j	$\lambda_j y_j$	λ_j	y_j	$\lambda_j y_j$	λ_j	y_j	$\lambda_j y_j$
I	1	1	1	0	1	0	0	1	0	−1	1	−1	−1	1	−1
II	1	0	0	1	1	1	1	1	1	0	1	0	0	1	0
III	1	1	1	0	0	0	0	1	0	−1	0	0	−1	0	0
IV	1	0	0	1	0	0	1	0	0	−1	0	0	−1	0	0
V	1	1	1	0	0	0	0	0	0	0	0	0	0	0	0
VI	1	0	0	1	1	1	1	0	0	−1	1	−1	−1	1	−1
VII	1	0	0	1	1	1	1	0	0	−1	1	−1	−1	0	0
VIII	1	1	1	0	1	0	0	1	0	−1	0	0	−1	1	−1
$\sigma = \Sigma \lambda_j y_j$	+4			+3			+1			+1			−1		
Output of R-element	1			1			1			1			0		
Result of recognition	incorrect			correct			incorrect			correct			incorrect		

	Step Number																	
	6			7			8			9			10			11		
Ordinal numbers of A-elements (planes)	Perceptron's state																	
	λ_j	y_j	$\lambda_j y_j$	λ_j	y_j	$\lambda_j y_j$	λ_j	y_j	$\lambda_j y_j$	λ_j	y_j	$\lambda_j y_j$	λ_j	y_j	$\lambda_j y_j$	λ_j	y_j	$\lambda_j y_j$
I	0	1	0	0	1	0	-1	1	-1	-1	1	-1	-1	1	-1	-1	1	-1
II	1	1	1	1	1	1	0	1	0	0	0	0	0	1	0	0	1	0
III	1	0	0	1	1	-1	2	0	0	2	1	2	2	0	0	2	1	2
IV	-1	1	-1	-1	0	0	-1	1	-1	-1	0	0	-1	1	-1	-1	0	0
V	0	0	0	0	1	0	-1	0	0	-1	0	0	-1	0	0	-1	0	0
VI	2	1	2	2	0	0	2	1	2	2	0	0	2	1	2	2	1	2
VII	1	1	1	1	0	0	-1	1	1	-1	0	0	-1	0	0	-1	1	1
VIII	0	1	0	0	1	0	-1	0	0	-1	1	-1	-1	1	-1	-1	1	-1
$\sigma = \Sigma \lambda_j y_j$	+4			0			+3			-4			+1			-1		
Output of R-element	1			1			1			0			1			0		
Result of recognition	correct			incorrect			correct			correct			correct			correct		

New values of λ_j are given in the first column of the second step.

Now the second object is presented (point 2 in Fig. 55). The Perceptron correctly relates it to the image b and the coefficients λ_j are unchanged. At the third step the Perceptron again makes a mistake which causes a new change of the coefficients λ_j. On the fourth step the Perceptron correctly recognizes a figure from image b and on the fifth step errs again so incurring a new change of λ_j (this time it is an increase). The sixth step gives a correct answer, the seventh an incorrect one, but beginning with the eight step the answers are correct.

If the sums $\Sigma\lambda_j y_j$ for all polyhedra are formed, it will be seen that after the seventh step the Perceptron has created the separating surface indicated in Fig. 55 by a heavy line. The polyhedra 11, 14, 15, 16, 19, 20 and 21 are attributed to image b, the remaining ones to image a.

There is a certain analogy between the performance of the Perceptron and the algorithm of dissecting planes. In both cases training leads to the creation of a separating surface approximated by fragments of planes.

4. THE PERCEPTRON'S ALGORITHM FROM THE STAND-POINT OF THE POTENTIAL METHOD

In the above we have treated the Perceptron's activity as the creation of a separating surface built from "fragments" of planes. However, another interpretation is also possible. The function σ on each step of the Perceptron's activity is positive (or equal to zero) in the part of the space which is related by the Perceptron to one image, negative in the part related to the other, and changes sign when crossing the separating surface (cf. Fig. 56, where in each polyhedron, values of the function σ are indicated after the seventh step). The function σ behaves like the function $\Phi = \Phi_a - \Phi_b$, which we have met with in the algorithm of potentials when dealing with the identification of two images.

The function σ depends on the coefficients λ_j and consequently, changes after each "error" committed by the Perceptron.

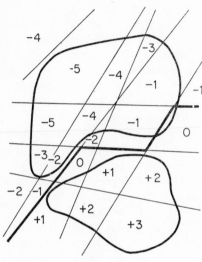

Fig. 56

Let us define the function

$$\Delta\sigma = \sigma' - \sigma$$

where $\sigma = \Sigma\lambda_j y_j$ prior to a certain stage of the Perceptron's activity and $\sigma' = \Sigma\lambda'_j y_j$ after that stage in which there was an incorrect answer, and the coefficients λ_j were changed to λ'_j.

Consider the structure of $\Delta\sigma$:

$$\Delta\sigma = \sigma' - \sigma = \sum_{j=1}^{m} \lambda'_j y_j - \sum_{j=1}^{m} \lambda_j y_j =$$
$$= \sum_{j=1}^{m} (\lambda'_j - \lambda_j) y_j = \sum_{j=1}^{m} \Delta\lambda_j y$$

Here the combination $y_1, y_2, \ldots, y_j, \ldots, y_m$ is the code of a given polyhedron and $\Delta\lambda_j = (\lambda'_j - \lambda_j)$ is the change of λ_j due to an incorrect response of the Perceptron after the point has fallen into this polyhedron.

In accordance with the second algorithm the only λ_j to be changed are those which correspond to the excited A-elements, i.e. the $\Delta\lambda_j$ are non-zero and equal $+1$ or -1 if, and only if, the y_j equal one. Thus the absolute value of $\Delta\sigma$ for a given polyhedron is equal to the number of A-elements excited when a point falls into this polyhedron.

Let us call the polyhedron into which a point has fallen "initial", and let us follow the changes of $|\Delta\sigma|$ when passing from the initial polyhedron to others. We shall move along straight lines in different directions away from the initial polyhedron. If we pass to an adjacent polyhedron by crossing the kth plane facing this new polyhedron by its "positive" side, the corresponding y_k changes from zero to one. The value of $|\Delta\sigma|$ remains unchanged, since $\Delta\lambda_k$ is zero (the kth A-element in the initial polyhedron was not excited). If, on the other hand, the transfer was effected through, say, the qth, plane facing by its "positive" side the initial polyhedron, then y_q decreases from one to zero and $|\Delta\sigma|$ decreases by one, for in this case $|\Delta\sigma_q| = 1$. Thus, when passing from the initial polyhedron to any other, $|\Delta\sigma|$ will be decreased by one on crossing any plane or will remain constant. The behaviour of $|\Delta\sigma|$ depends on which side of the crossed plane was facing the initial polyhedron: "positive" or "negative". This rule is very easily followed in Fig. 57, where $|\Delta\sigma|$ are computed for all polyhedra as in the seventh step of our example, when the seventh point has fallen into the seventh polyhedron.

As follows from this figure, the absolute value of $\Delta\sigma$ is maximal in the initial, seventh, polyhedron and decreases away from it.

The function $\Delta\sigma$ does not depend on the state of the Perceptron in the training process. Indeed, the values of y_j

for each polyhedron are fixed when the connections of receptors to A-elements are being made, and remain unchanged afterwards, and the $\Delta\lambda_j$ are determined exclusively by values of y_j in the initial polyhedron.

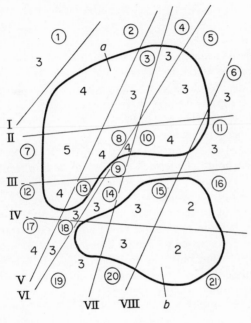

Fig. 57

Thus, as soon as receptors are connected to A-elements (which happens prior to the experiment), to every polyhedron (say, the lth) there is related a certain function $\Delta_l\sigma$ generally speaking, different for different polyhedra. Every $\Delta_l\sigma$ is maximal in "own" (lth) polyhedron and decreases away from it. Hence, these functions are analogous to the functions φ used in the algorithm of potentials with the difference that the φ's are defined solely by the distance from the source-point, whereas the $\Delta_i\sigma$'s depend also on the relative position of polyhedra in the receptor space.

In the training process the function σ is created by consecutive algebraic summation ($+$ if errors occur on the points of one image, and $-$ if errors occur on the points of the other image) of the functions $\Delta_i\sigma$ — exactly as the function $\Delta\Phi$ is created from functions φ in the algorithm of potentials.

There is therefore a basic similarity between the mode of operation of the Perceptron and the algorithm of potentials in the receptor space.[1] And since this algorithm is based on the compactness hypothesis, one can conjecture that the principles underlying the Perceptron are closely related to this property of images.

When discussing the performance of the Perceptron from the point of view of the algorithm of potentials we put no restrictions on the planes realized by A-elements. We were not concerned with their coordinates nor with the directions of their "positive" sides. The only requirement was that if we were to move along an arbitrary straight line in the receptor space we should intersect a sufficient number of planes "from plus side to minus side". In other words, we required that in the receptor space there were sufficiently many randomly oriented planes.

If this condition is satisfied, then different Perceptrons with different connections between receptors and A-elements would produce practically the same separating surfaces when trained to recognize the same images. The outcome of the Perceptron's training does not depend to any appreciable extent on destruction of some connections between the receptors and A-elements, or on switching off some

---

[1] The apparent difference that functions φ and $\Delta\Phi$ are continuous whereas functions $\Delta\sigma$ and σ change step-like (on the sides of polyhedra) is immaterial, because of the very large number of polyhedra which exist due to intersections of the few hundred planes constructed by the Perceptron.

A-elements. Indeed, the destruction of the connection "receptor to A-element" is equivalent to changing one coefficient of one of the dissecting planes, i.e. to a certain shift of this plane. The switching-off of an A-element is equivalent to the deletion of one dissecting plane.

Provided the number of destroyed connections, or of switched-off A-elements is not too large, these operations cannot substantially change the more or less uniform division

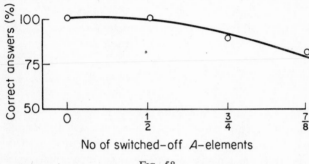

No of switched-off A-elements

Fig. 58

of the space into a large number of polyhedra, and thus cannot substantially influence the process of learning and its outcome. From this point of view, the random connection between receptors and A-elements should be considered as a technically convenient realization of a sufficiently uniform division of the receptor space.

The Perceptron proves to be quite stable with respect to structural changes effected not necessarily prior to the training process. If some connections "receptor — A-element" are destroyed, or if some A-elements are switched off in an already "trained" Perceptron, the reliability of recognition decreases very slowly, even with quite serious destruction. For example, Fig. 58 shows the influence of the number of switched-off A-elements on the reliability of functioning of a Perceptron trained to recognize the letters

E and X. Even when 7/8 of all the A-elements are switched-off, the reliability of recognition does not fall below 80%. Such a behaviour is made possible by the fact that deletion of dissecting planes decrease the "quality" of the separating surface by decreasing the number of polyhedra and by increasing their average size, but does not seriously distort the Perceptron's mode of functioning.

2. PAPA

Let us consider the Perceptron's activity from yet another standpoint. As previously stated, the state of the jth A-element depends on the sign of the expression.

$$\sum_{i=1}^{n} r_{ij} x_i - \Theta$$

In this expression the quantity x_i corresponds to the state of the ith receptor and equals one if it is excited. The quantities r_{ij} for some receptors (those that are not connected to the jth A-element) equal zero; for the remaining receptors they assume values $+1$ or -1 depending on the sign of the connection between a given receptor and a given A-element.

All receptors connected with a given A-element may thus be divided into two groups, depending on the sign of the connections. Receptors of each group form certain mozaics ("pattern") in the receptor field. When a figure is shown to the Perceptron those receptors (within each pattern) are excited onto which a fragment of the contour is being projected. The x_i's corresponding to these receptors become equal to one (the remaining x_i's of each pattern correspond to unexcited receptors, and thus equal zero). Let the number of excited receptors of the first, "positive" pattern be K_j, and the number of excited receptors of the second, "negative", pattern be Q_j. Then the expression describing the state of jth A-element assumes the form

$$K_j - Q_j - \Theta.$$

The A-element will be excited if

$$(K_j - Q_j) > \Theta.$$

Thus, to each A-element of the Perceptron there correspond two patterns in the receptors field: a "positive" one and a "negative" one. The state of the A-element is defined by the number of receptors excited by the figure presented in each of these two patterns.

This interpretation of the A-element performance underlies the simple explanation of the action of a cognitive machine called PAPA (from the Italian for Automatic Probabilistic Programme Analyzer for Pattern Recognition) proposed by an Italian scientist A. Gamba. This machine, a diagram of which is shown in Fig. 59 has fundamental principles similar to those of the Perceptron of Fig. 52. The difference consists in the manner of realization of A-elements: in PAPA A-elements act sequentially in contrast to the Perceptron, wherein all A-elements act simultaneously. Each stage of the machine's activity corresponding to the recognition of one figure is thus sub-divided into a sequence of "small" stages in each of which only one A-element is active.

The machine performs as follows: Patterns (mozaics) are generated by a tape recorder (TR) on whose tape a random function ("noise") is recorded. The recorded function is reproduced during each recognition and transmitted in the form of a variable voltage onto the control electrodes of a cathode ray tube (CRT). This function is time-wise divided into a number of intervals, each corresponding to a "small" step, i.e. to one A-element. (In Fig. 59, the signal, conventionally represented as a curve, is divided into four steps.) Controlled by this signal the light-spot on the CRT screen draws random curves — "patterns". The light-spot image is projected, by an optical system, L, onto the object presented to the machine. The object is presented as a transparent figure on the opaque mask, M. The quantity of light

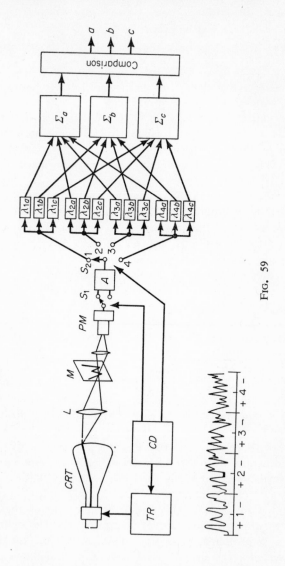

FIG. 59

passed through the mask during a certain interval of time is proportional to the number of intersections of the figure contour with a particular "pattern" drawn in the same time by the light-spot projection on the mask. If one measures the quantity of light, k_j, passed through the mask during the first half of the jth small step, and the quantity of light q_j, passed through the mask during the second half of the same small step and subtracts one from another, then the difference $k_j - q_j$ will be equivalent to the difference $K_j - Q_j$. This operation is performed by a photo-multiplier PM and accumulator A, connected to the output of PM through a switch S_1. The switch S_1 is controlled by a device, CD, so that in the first half of any small-step the output signal from PM is transmitted to the "positive" input of A, and on the second half to the "negative" input of the accumulator A. During each step the accumulator generates the difference $k_j - q_j$ and compares it with the threshold value θ. If $k_j - q_j < \theta$ the output signal of the accumulator equals one, otherwise it equals zero.

Therefore, on each small step the system "tape recorder — cathode ray tube — photo-multiplier — accumulator" realizes one A-element. The remaining part of the scheme is very similar to that of the Perceptron (cf. Fig. 52). The only difference is that the multplication of output signals from the accumulator by coefficients λ and the addition by adders of the products so obtained is performed sequentially. To achieve this, the output of the accumulator A is connected to amplifiers λ through the switch S_2 whose position always agrees with the ordinal number of the current small step. The comparison of output signals of the adders and the identification of the object presented is performed after a full sequence of small steps is finished, i.e. when all A-elements have been activated.

Training, i.e. the changing of co-efficients λ_j may be carried out according to any of the algorithms developed for the Perceptron of Fig. 52.

The cognitive machine so described possesses some very important advantages. Firstly, a large number (several hundred) of A-elements are replaced by a single though complicated device comprising a tape-recorder, cathode ray tube, photo-multiplier and accumulator. This substantially simplifies the machine and reduces its physical size. The PAPA is of desk-top size, whereas the MARK-1 comprises several man-sized racks. Secondly in the PAPA it is very easy to increase the number of "receptors", i.e. to decrease the

| 5Y | 3Y4S | 2Y3E | 5E4S | 1E2S | 2E3S | 4E3S | 3Y1E | 3Y | 2E | 3Y4E | 3S |

FIG. 60

"grain-size" of figures presented and thus to increase the accuracy of recognition. The number of "receptors" in PAPA equals the ratio of area of the mask to the area of the light-spot projected onto it. In order to increase the number of receptors, it is only necessary to reduce the size of the light-spot; this can easily be achieved either by better focusing of the ray or by tuning the projecting system. In the Perceptron, on the other hand, one would have to increase the actual number of elements in the retina and the number of A-elements, in other words to complicate the machine.

A shortcoming of the PAPA is that sequential activation of A-elements generally increases the necessary duration of "inspection" of each figure shown. However, the speed of the system "CRT−PM−A" may be made so high, that the exposure time of each object would be sufficiently small.

In what follows we shall describe a "pocket Perceptron" proposed by Gamba, a quite effective demonstration model of a cognitive machine, capable of distinguishing three letters, Y, E, S. The description will be given so that the reader will be able to use Fig. 60 as a model.

The model consists of 12 rectangular windows. On each of the windows "random curves" of two types — heavy and light — are drawn. These lines represent "positive" and "negative" patterns.[1]

Thus, our pocket Perceptron has 12 A-elements. Underneath each of the windows there are numbers with indices

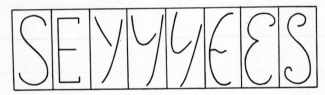

FIG. 61

corresponding to the objects to be distinguished. These numbers represent the λ co-efficients (the model is presented in the trained state with λ's already accumulated).

In order to conduct an experiment in recognition, draw on a piece of tracing paper, a rectangular window equal to those of the model and write in it one of the letters Y, E or S. The horizontal and vertical dimensions of the letter should be approximately equal to dimensions of the window, as in Fig. 61.

The tracing paper is placed over the first window of the model so that the contours of both windows coincide. Now compute the number of intersections of the letter with "heavy" and "light" patterns. If the contour of the letter intersects the heavy pattern more times than the light one, then the numbers written beneath the first rectangle are written in the first row of Table XX, all numbers being

[1] Has the reader observed that the patterns in Fig. 60 form the English words: RANDOM LINES?

recorded in the columns corresponding to their indices. If the letter intersects the heavy pattern fewer times than the light one, the numbers are not recorded in the table.[2] After this the letter is placed over the second rectangle, and depending on the number of intersections with heavy and light patterns, the numbers written beneath this window either are, or are not, recorded in the second row of Table XX.

TABLE XX

Window Number	Y	E	S
1			
2			
.			
.			
.			
11			
12			

Having performed this operation with all windows of the model we compute the sums of numbers recorded in each column of the table. The pocket Perceptron recognizes a letter if one of these sums happens to be bigger than the other two.

One can easily check that the model indeed recognizes various denotations of the letters Y, E and S.

As already stated, the model is shown here in the trained state. This means that the numbers written beneath each of the windows result from a certain sequence of experiments in which various denotations of the letters Y, E and S have been shown to the model. The training algorithm used was quite similar to that used with the PAPA. After training, the smallest λ for each A-element has been rejected, and the

[2] This corresponds to the performance of an A-element when $\theta = 0$.

remainder divided by a constant factor. Thus even though the model recognizes three letters, to each A-element there corresponds only one or two λ coefficients; the remainder are zero. The reader may train the model himself and obtain a new combination of λ's possibly different from Fig. 60 that will guarantee sufficiently reliable recognition.

6. THE PERCEPTRON AS A MODEL OF THE BRAIN

At the beginning of this chapter we said that in developing the Perceptron Rosenblatt attempted to model some properties of the living brain. We can now discuss which particular significant properties of the brain are modelled in the Perceptron.

Firstly, in contrast to the algorithms considered earlier, the Perceptron's algorithm does not require the memorizing of all (or some) objects during training, nor does it require comparison with all "known" objects when recognizing a new one (as is done in the potentials algorithm when evaluating the function Φ). In this sense, the Perceptron's mode of functioning is definitely similar to that of the brain, which forms ideas of images presented without memorizing individual objects, and recognizes new objects without comparing them with all those previously encountered.

Furthermore, the Perceptron's structure has some features in common with the structure of higher nervous systems. In particular, the Perceptron's receptors are a close enough analogy of the receptors of the visual apparatus, and A-elements have a certain similarity to neurons. It is a well known fact, that neurons have the property of being excited if the intensity of the signal they receive from connected receptors (or other neurons) exceeds a certain threshold value.

The property of the Perceptron comprising the random connection of receptors and A-elements resembles, apparently, analogical features of brain-structure. It is quite probable that the connections between neurons in the brain are in the majority of cases also random, i.e. vary between individuals of the same species. If we supposed the converse, i.e. that all connections between neurons are fixed and thus are identical for all individuals of a given species, and that changing this structure leads to severe perturbations in the functioning of the brain, then we would have to accept that the information about these connections is transmitted by hereditary means. Since the number of neurons in the brain is measured in milliards this last assumption leads to a fantastically large amount of genetic information.

At the same time the Perceptron exemplifies how biologically natural is the notion of compactness since learning to recognize compact sets proves to be compatible with random connections between receptors and neurons.

It is known that the brain is capable of preserving or restoring its many functions even in cases of severe destruction caused by traumas or sickness. With respect to partial destruction of its structure (cf. Fig. 58) the stability of the Perceptron shows a marked similarity with this property of the brain.

It does not of course follow from all this that the algorithm of the brain and of the Perceptron are identical. However, at the present time the Perceptron is, apparently, the most probable model of the brain.

Chapter 6

POSSIBLE WAYS OF FURTHER
IMPROVEMENT OF COGNITIVE MACHINES

The cognitive machines described in previous chapters simulate that learning process for which the following properties may be considered to be characteristic:

(a) The objects to be recognized are situated more or less in one part of the receptor field ("centred"), are approximately the same size and are approximately identically oriented.

(b) Man is a necessary partner in the learning process: he performs the *a priori* classification of the objects used during the training period and presents the results of this classification to the machine.

(c) The objects recognized are sufficiently simple in a general intuitive sense.

However, the nature of real learning processes is considerably richer than the models considered.

In reality we successfully classify objects situated in an arbitrary part of our field of vision, having various dimensions and differently oriented[1] (cf. Fig. 62).

Beside this, the processes of learning to classify do not necessarily presuppose participation of a "teacher". Suppose we ask an illiterate man or a child to sort out mixed representations of objects of various images (say, a deck of cards with numerals drawn on them) into groups of "similar"

---

[1] Except in cases when a change of orientation transforms one object into another, as, e.g. with Cyrillic letters E and Ш, Roman letters p and d, or Arabic numerals 6 and 9.

objects. This task will be successfully completed, even though the performer may receive no information regarding the correctness of his action. As another example, consider the "abstract" figures presented in Fig. 63. The reader is asked to divide them into two groups, in such a way that each

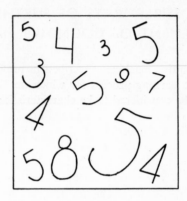

FIG. 62

group contains objects more "similar" than objects from the other. If the reader performs this experiment with a number of his friends, he will convince himself that the majority of "experimenters" will divide the objects in an identical way (figures 1, 4 and 5 will be attributed to one group, figures 2, 3 and 6 to another).

And finally, we are naturally capable of learning to distinguish objects much more complicated than letters or numerals, e.g. "different portraits of the same man" (including caricatures) "men's portraits", "women's portraits", etc.

In order to bring machine learning processes closer to reality a number of problems have to be solved, particularly recognition of differently oriented figures and of figures of different sizes, identification without a "teacher" and recognition of complex images.

At the present time we are not able to solve these problems. However, in principle, the possibility of solving these problems is not in doubt. The aim of this chapter is to formulate these problems and sketch some possible ways of attacking them.

FIG. 63

1. CENTERING FIGURES AND THEIR REDUCTION TO STANDARD SIZE AND ORIENTATION

To begin with, let us consider the following simplest case: Assume that the machine is to recognize printed letters from the same type-face, uniformly oriented but of various sizes and appearing in various parts of the receptor field. At any one moment there is only one letter in the field.

In this case the recognition process may be performed in the following way. The machine records one typical sample of each letter and transforms these samples in such a manner that all have the same vertical dimensions and all their centres of gravity coincide. When the same transformation is performed on an unknown object it will coincide with one of the stored samples, and thus recognition will be effected.

However, even with a very small complication of the problem this approach fails. Indeed, if there is a very small perturbation present on the field besides the projection of the letter to be recognized (e.g. one receptor lying above the letter's contour is excited), then the machine will take for the vertical dimension not the true height of the letter but this height plus the distance from the topmost part of the letter's contour to the receptor excited by the perturbation. The figure so transformed will not coincide with any of the stored samples and thus will not be recognized.

So the procedure described fails even in fairly simple cases; for solving the general problem of constructing cognitive machines its value is even more limited.

Evidently the problem of centering and of normalizing the dimensions of figures generates a vicious circle: in order to recognize a figure it should be transformed, but in order to effect correct transformation the figure should be first recognized, so that the perturbations can be disregarded.

However, a possible way out of this difficulty can be suggested.

Let us state the problem more precisely. Denote by $S(0, 0, 0, 1)$ a point in the receptor space corresponding to a certain figure, and by $S(x, y, \psi, k)$ the point corresponding to the same figure shifted by magnitude of x horizontally, by y vertically, turned around by angle ψ and subject to a similarity transformation with co-efficient k, i.e. "stretched" or "contracted" so that the distance between any two points in the receptor field is increased or decreased k times. Then all possible shifts, rotations and scale changes of any figure can be described by four quantities x, y, ψ and k. The problem is to find x, y, ψ and k for each figure so that it can be recognized correctly.

One possible solution of this problem may be described as follows. The first figure appearing in the training process is not transformed. Corresponding to it the point $S_1(0, 0, 0, 1)$ is taken as the source of potential of the type considered in Chapter 4. Now the second figure appears. At the corresponding point S_2, a potential φ_{12} is generated by the point S_1. If the new figure is subject to all possible transformations, i.e. if the quantities x, y, ψ and k assume all possible values, the point $S_2(x_2, y_2, \psi_2, k_2)$ will move in the receptor space. The potential φ_{12} generated at S_2 by S_1 will change depending on the values of x_2, y_2, ψ_2, k_2. In other words, φ_{12} will be a function of the four parameters x_2, y_2, ψ_2, k_2. We search for values of these parameters, for which φ_{12} is maximized. This operation is known as maximization of the functions φ_{12}. Thus the second figure, independent of which image it belongs to, is transformed in such a way as to maximize the potential φ_{12} generated at $S_2(x_2, y_2, \psi_2, k_2)$ by S_1. The co-ordinates of S_2 which correspond to the maximum of φ_{12} are recorded, and S_2 is taken as the second source of potential.

The third figure is transformed in such a way as to maximize the potential φ_{123} generated by the first two points at the point $S_3(x_3, y_3, \psi_3, k_3)$ etc.

Such a transformation of figures apparently leads to the following results. The points corresponding to the same image as S_1 will be drawn into a compact group in the vicinity of S_1. In addition, the distance between corresponding points is proportional to the difference between figures. In particular, the points corresponding to geometrically similar figures coincide. The points of any remaining images will also be drawn together into clusters and these clusters will be drawn close to each other.

After this transformation has been completed, the transformed figures are treated as precursors and the training algorithm described in Chapter 4 is applied to them. As a result, potentials $\Phi_a, \Phi_b, \ldots, \Phi_m$ are constructed in the receptor space for each image: $a, b, \ldots m$. Since the transformation described above draws points of each image close together and thus increases point-density, the potentials will have comparatively sharp peaks, i.e. that form which is most convenient for separation of sets.

The recognition of a new object is performed by determining to which image the object can best be "fitted". For this purpose the potential $\Phi_{a(1)}$ generated at the first unknown point $S_{(1)}(x_{(1)}, y_{(1)}, \psi_{(1)}, k_{(1)})$ by image a is maximized, then the potential $\Phi_{b(1)}$ generated at this point by image b is maximized, etc. The maxima are compared and the object is attributed to the image which generates the largest possible potential at its corresponding point.

It should be noted that the method of solution of the stated problem has been outlined above only very briefly and the problem cannot be considered as solved. The main obstacle is that existing methods of maximizing functions can be applied only to certain classes of functions. Which of these methods may be applied in any given case can only be ascertained by experiment. It is quite possible that our problem will require a new, special method of maximization.

2. LEARNING WITHOUT REWARD

By "learning without reward" we shall understand machine-learning without the participation of a "teacher", i.e. in our case, learning to identify images without introducing information about the classification of objects presented during learning or information regarding the correctness of the machine's answers.

The figures presented in Fig. 63 have been taken from two different classes to which correspond two different compact sets (the method of producing such figures was given in Chapter 2).

In correctly sorting these figures, the reader may have noted that (in common with most people) he acted without reward, i.e. he had no information concerning the correctness of his actions. Apparently, one's action is based solely on the fact that the points corresponding to these figures form two separated groups in the receptor space.

FIG. 64

If asked to draw a line separating two isolated groups of points (Fig. 64) one would do it without difficulty. But it would be quite difficult, even impossible, to tell how one did it, i.e. to describe the algorithm for constructing the separating line. If such an algorithm for the separating of compact groups of points could be formulated in a sufficiently clear and detailed form, the problem of learning to recognize images without rewards would probably be solved. However for this problem it is necessary to divide into parts a multidimensional set about which nothing is known except that it comprises several compact groups. The general algorithm of such a separation is not known. In a very special case when the distance between two compact sets[1] is

---

[1] The distance between two sets is the distance between the two closest points belonging to different sets.

much greater than one, the division algorithm can be described as follows. After receiving a sufficient number of objects (their classification being unknown) the machine chooses one of the points corresponding to these objects. Then the machine finds among the remaining points one which is closest to the first point. This point is indexed by a number equal to the distance between the first and second point. Then a point is found which is closest to the two-pointset. This point is indexed by a number equal to distance between the two-point set and the third point, etc.

As the result of this procedure all points will be found first, which belong to the same set as the initially chosen point. Then the machine will pass to points of the second set, and the index of the first object of the second image will be considerably greater than all preceding indices. The occurrence of such a large index indicates that all points of the first image have been accounted for and that all the remaining points belong to another image.

3. RECOGNITION OF COMPLEX IMAGES SINGLING OUT CHARACTERISTIC FEATURES

The division of images into simple and complex is to a certain extent conventional. It is intuitively clear, for example, that the image "numeral 5" may be considered more complex than the image "numeral 1" and the image "letter Ж" even more complex, but it is not possible to define precisely the border between simple and complex images.

The images which can be recognized by the machines described in preceding chapters were considered "simple" because none of them possessed any concrete properties except compactness; or rather there was no need to take such properties into account in order to recognize them, e.g. one did not need to divide these images into smaller elements.

However, it is not likely that the compactness property will be sufficient to enable objects of any complexity to be identified.

If we consider for example, the numeral 5 as a complex image and try to describe it, the description will probably be something like this: "at the top a horizontal dash; at the top left a straight angle and a vertical stroke; in the

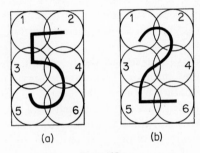

(a)   (b)

FIG. 65

middle an angle; in the bottom half, an oval to the right and a discontinuity to the left", and so on. The description will consist of a list of elements of the figure (i.e. of figures more simple than the initial one) and some indications concerning their mutual orientation. Such a description represents, in principle, a collection of certain characteristic features of the figure described. One can assume that the solution of the problem of how to train the machine to recognize complex objects is presented in the form of an algorithm for singling out characteristic features. When such an algorithm is constructed it will be necessary to isolate such characteristic features of objects presented during training and to "observe" them in unknown objects during recognition.

At the present time there are no papers which would illuminate this task[1].

We think, however, that separation of characteristic features would be made much easier if we were to accept that characteristic features have the two following properties:

(a) A characteristic feature is a part of a figure that can be isolated by a "window" of simple shape, e.g. circular.

(b) Each characteristic feature is an image as defined in preceding chapters.

Proceeding from these assumptions one could sketch the following rough draft of the algorithm for the separation of characteristic features and the recognition of complex figures.

The figures projected on the receptor field are received part by part by means of "windows" superimposed on the field (Fig. 65). During training, elements of figures appearing in each of the windows are considered to be images and one of the known algorithms is applied to them. As a result the simple figures appearing in each of the windows are classified into a certain number of simple images — *characteristic features*. In the example shown in Fig. 65 there are seven such characteristic features:

(a) An angle with the vortex upwards and to the left.
(b) A horizontal dash.
(c) An angle with the vortex downwards and to the left.
(d) An arc convex to the right and upwards.
(e) An arc convex to the left and downwards.
(f) An arc convex to the right and downwards.
(g) An arc convex to the left and upwards.

If the "windows" are numbered as in Fig. 65, a complex image 5 will be represented as the code "abcdef", and the

---

[1] Since this monograph was written, a number of publications dealing with the problem have in fact appeared in press. (Transl. footnote.)

complex image 2 as the code "gdgfcb" (here a, b, . . . , g are conventional denotations of characteristic features, and the sequencing of symbols in the code from the left to the right corresponds to the numbering of the windows). Training is completed by storing such codes for all complex images which are to be recognized. When an unknown figure is presented, its characteristic features are recognized as objects of simple images and the code composed from them is compared with codes recorded in the machine memory.

It might be that the method outlined will be more effective than the direct application of the algorithms considered in preceding chapters.

RECOMMENDED LITERATURE

1. Rosenblatt F., Perceptron Simulation Experiments. *Proceedings of the IRE*, **48**, No. 3. (1960).

2. Hay J. C., Martin F. C., and Wightman C, W., The Mark I Perceptron — design and performance, *IRE Intern. Conv. Rec.* **8**, No. 2 (1960) 78—87.

3. Braverman E. M., Experiments in teaching a machine to recognize visual images. *Automation & Remote Control* **23**, No. 3 (1962) 315—327.

4. Aizerman M. A., Experiments in teaching machines to recognize visual images, Biologicheskie aspekty kibernetiki (Biological aspects of cybernetics) Soviet Academy of Sciences Publishing House, Moscow, 1962.

5. Glushkov V. M., The theory of teaching a class of discrete Perceptrons, *Zhurnal Vychislitelnoi Matematiki i Matematicheskoi Fiziki*, **2**, No. 2, (1962).

6. Gamba A., Palmieri G. and Sanna R., Preliminary experimental results with PAPA. 2, *Supplemento al Nuovo Cimento*, vol. **23** serie X, pp. 280—284.

7. Bledsoe W. W., and Browning I., Pattern recognition and reading by machine, Proceedings Eastern Joint Computer Conference 1959.

8. Highleyman W. H., and Kamentsky L. A., Comments on a character recognition method of Bledsoe and Browning, *IRE Transaction on Electronic Computer*, vol. EC—9 No. 2 1960.

9. Sebestyen G. S., "Decision-making Processes in Pattern Recognition". The Macmillan Company, New York (1962).

10. Sebestyen G. S., Pattern recognition by an adaptive process of sample set construction. *IRE Transaction on Information Theory*, vol. IT—8 No. 5 (1962).

11. Highleyman W. H., Linear decision function with application to pattern recognition. *Proceedings of the IRE*, **50**, No. 6 (1960).

12. Marill T., and Green D. M., Statistical recognition function and the design of pattern recognizers. *IRE Transaction on Electronic Computer*. EC—9 No. 4 (1960).

13. Abramson N., and Braverman D., Learning to recognize patterns in a random environment. *IRE Transaction on Information Theory*, IT—8, No. 5, 1962.

14. Bongard M. M., Modelling of recognition process in counting machine, *Biofizica*, **6**, No. 2, (1961).

15. Brailovskii V. L., On a method of recognizing objects which are described by several parameters, and its possible applications, *Automation & Remote Control*, **23**, No. 12, 1962/1542—1551.

16. Kharkevich, A. A., Image recognition, *Radiotekhnika* **14**, No. 5, (1959).

17. Kharkevich A. A., On construction principles of reading machines, *ibid.* **15**, No. 2, (1960).

18. Reading devices. Proceedings of the Conference on Information Processing, Machine Translation, and Automatic Text reading, Moscow, (1962).

19. Petrenko, A. I., and Sviechnikov S. V., Basic trends in the development of reading automata, Izvestia Vuzov: *Radiotekhnika*, **4**, No. 3, (1961).

20. Fain V. S., On construction principles of an image recognizing machine, *Radiotekhnika*, **15**, No. 3, (1960).

21. Garmash V. A., Pereverzev-Orlov, V. S., and Cirlin V. M., On a quasi-topological method of letter recognition, *Izvestia AN SSSR, OTN, Energetika i avtomatika*, No. 3 (1960).

22. Pereverzev-Orlov V. S., Polakov V. G., On a construction of a reading machine, *Izvestia AN SSSR, OTN, Energetika i avtomatika*, No. 3, (1961).

23. Steinbuch K., Automatische Zeichenerkennung Teil. *Nachrichtentechnik Z.* **11**, No. 4, No. 5, (1958).

24. Kovalevskii V. A., A correlative method of image recognition, *Zhur. Vych. Mat. i Mat. Fiz.* **2**, No. 4, (1962).

25. Eliseer V. K. and Kovalevskii V. A., Research on an algorithm for recognition of typed symbols, *ibid.*, **2** No. 5, (1962).

26. Jarbus, A. L., The eye motion in observing complex objects, *Biofizika*, **6**, No. 2 (1961).

27. Feldbaum A. A., Computing devices in automatic systems, *Fizmatgiz*, Moscow—Leningrad (1959).

28. Aizerman M. A., Braverman E. M., and Rozonoer, L. I., Theoretical principles of potential functions method in the problem of teaching automata to recognize classes. *Automation & Remote Control.* **25**, No. 6, (1964) 821—837.